FROM THE SLOPES OF OLYMPUS

TO THE BANKS OF THE LEA

Published by Smoke: a London Peculiar, 2013

© 2013 Smoke: a London Peculiar

The copyright in individual contributions remains with
the respective authors, artists or photographers.

Smoke: a London Peculiar
www.smokealondonpeculiar.co.uk

ISBN 978-0-9575680-0-6

Printed by Barnwell Print Ltd
Dunkirk, Aylsham, Norwich, NR11 6SU

From the Slopes of Olympus to the Banks of the Lea

a book by

Smoke: a London Peculiar

Edited by Jude Rogers and Matt Haynes

Smoke 18

Alex
Farebrother
-Naylor

IT'S A LITTLE BEFORE NOON, and we're standing around a huge, glowing screen in the office next door. Baguettes for lunch, then, I joke to my colleagues, adjusting my metaphorical beret, getting ready to play down my disappointment. And then Jacques Rogge says London. I am Steve Cram, Kelly Holmes and David Beckham. I am the child that jumped for Seoul and Barcelona, the teenager who boxed for Atlanta and Sydney, the young woman who sailed for Athens, and will row for Beijing. Everyone else in the room beams and bounces too, apart from one person, who is shaking his head. It's going to be a waste of money, he grumps. And a waste of time, too. Oh, rubbish, I tut comically, and tell him to shush. London is the right city for these games – what a city, it's *our* city – already bringing people together from every corner of the world. It's a good place, a *strong* place, a place where anything can happen. Lunch is a pint, and then another, and I stay at my boyfriend's the next morning to sleep off my hangover.

IT'S A LITTLE AFTER SIX, and the train that will take me home across south London is just pulling into Woolwich Arsenal station. I've seen tired faces pushed against the windows of coaches arriving on the Kent-bound platform, but few people are heading into town at this time, and I find a seat easily. Abandoned *Standards* are scattered across the carriage; this train has already made the long slow loop out of the city via Eltham and Bexleyheath, and now it's heading back to Cannon Street to scoop up another load. The front page drooped over the seat opposite catches my eye: *WE'VE WON*, says the headline, *HISTORIC VICTORY FOR BRITAIN*. Won? Won what? The Olympics? But wasn't Paris meant to be a shoo-in? I reach across. Beneath a photo of Kelly Holmes, smaller text offers confirmation: *Capital pips Paris in dramatic vote*. We slump into Woolwich Dockyard's gloomy platforms. If I press my cheek to the glass, blue July sky is just visible above the rain-stained brick of the retaining wall. Olympics, eh? Who'd have bloody thought…

Stratford Marsh
Wednesday, 6th July 2005

LONDON ATTACKS

Helen Sandler

for Jane

We have erected the new hammock stand in the kitchen. The weather is changeable despite your protestations that it's July. It seems that the British climate is still a maritime one even though we have been part of Europe for some decades now and might reasonably expect an improvement. So a South American multicoloured double hammock with own stand might be a bit extravagant and optimistic for a North London couple but that is what you've ordered, on the basis that it comes via a family firm of women and dogs in Kirkcudbright in Galloway, involved no child labour, and is fair trade. You show me a picture of the women and dogs lounging in a gigantic hammock, creatures of leisure – as well they may be if they're importing cheap hammocks and selling them for £173 each to the English.

You didn't ask me if I wanted to spend that kind of money on a hammock but you have a good get-out there, that you are happy to pay for it yourself. And then just that you are happy. You seem very happy and it is contagious, as we clamber nervously into the hammock which unfurls like a reverse chrysalis to wrap itself back around us. You push your legs against mine, we giggle, wriggle, sway, panic and grin as we try to find a way to lie down in it together.

You wonder if we can watch TV from the hammock.

There is to be a TV news special tonight called *London Attacks*.

That sounds brilliant, I say, like *Mars Attacks*. Perhaps it will be a spoof. Londoners will attack Paris and steal the Olympics from them. Do you think it was Parisians that did the terrorism? Maybe they hate us because we got the Olympics?

You are not taking any notice, staring at the carnage on the screen. What gets me, you say gravely, is that some people have this every day.

I feel irritated because I think you are avoiding the fact that you could easily have been on that tube train this morning; that you are zooming out to the global issue without taking a moment to allow just how local it is. But of course you are right, too, and I say nothing.

The Mayor says these are attacks on ordinary working-class Londoners, black and white, Hindu and Christian, Muslim and Jew. This has a ring to it but leaves out middle-class atheists who must make up about 50% of the dead and injured. He also wants the bombers to know that if they come and look at our airports and seaports (which doesn't seem like a good thing to encourage bombers to do), they will see people still pouring in to live in London and be themselves in the big city, escaping the rules that the bombers want to impose on them.

Has he lost the plot? Poor old Ken, yesterday he won the Olympics, and now this.

The US president contrasts the evil bombers with the heroic G8 who are ending world hunger, climate change and AIDS at Gleneagles. The prime minister makes a Churchillian speech above which the words Dunkirk Spirit are hovering. The men of the G8 line up behind him, like tin soldiers of the world.

I can't tell what's real any more. Between news programmes, the *Ground Force* team are joking in the garden with Nelson Mandela. He tells Charlie Dimmock she looks like a Spice Girl. I ask you whether Nelson Mandela lives in England now and you say it might be the African garden outside the British Museum. What, I say, is it his garden? Does he sit there all day? Yes, you say, you can wave to him from the Number 7 bus as you go by. Then it's the news again with pictures of the blown-up double-decker with the seats still there and people's insides spattered on the nearest building.

We go up to bed with the cat padding ahead of us. You are both asleep in minutes, side by side, but I give up and trudge back downstairs. In the semi-darkness, the hammock fills the kitchen like a colourful ship that has sailed in from the garden, or an ark we've slaved to build.

I climb aboard. It's different without you. The fabric closes round me like a shroud.

8/7/05, 01:00

Welcome to Stratford, Host City

Marshlands

Matt Haynes

I grew up around here.

On page thirty-seven of my old *A-to-Z*, in the wordless, fingermarked space between East India Dock and the reservoirs at Walthamstow, spider-black train tracks curl over ravelled skeins of water that fray across the page like cracks in yellowed plaster.

I grew up around here, on the margins of these marshes where wide-eyed dreams of Wembley Way were played out each Sunday morning on eighty-eight back-to-back pitches; and across which, on winter afternoons when Orient were at home, four smudged halos of light glimmered through the mist.

I grew up around here.

On Wednesdays, a council bus would take us from school to the edge of the marsh, for football or hockey or cross-country runs beside the hump-shunting yards. And, as we ran, shivering, trying to out-sprint each uncoupled wagon as it gathered pace down the smooth earth slope, gravity driving it into its chosen berth via a deftly flicked set of points, we would see, across the rainy wastes beyond the goal posts, the seven grey towers of the Trowbridge Estate, monumental gateways to the city beyond.

East of the towers, back on our side of the marsh, was Stratford. For those of us from further up the Central Line, Stratford was just where you changed trains for Ilford, Romford or – in summer – Southend-on-Sea. There was no DLR back then, no Jubilee, no Silverlink to Dalston, just an odd little line alongside the river on which, once every two hours, dusty, yellow-faced diesels from North Woolwich crept out past the filter beds and desolate Lea Bridge station into the pylon-strung, wind-humming emptiness beyond.

Stratford was stranded on the wrong bank of the Lea, the East Saxon shore; to reach London meant crossing the no man's land of the marshes. Soon, though, in a neat reversal of fortune, it seems that American tourists will arrive at Shakespeare's birthplace only to be told that they've got the wrong one. Soon, our Stratford, the real Stratford, will be just two hours from a brioche and a chocolat chaud at the Gare du Nord. Soon, our Stratford will be part of History.

The seven towers at Hackney Wick were dynamited years ago. The marshalling yard at Temple Mills made way for displaced Spitalfields. And Brisbane Road's skeletal pylons became modern lo-lighters, no longer polluting the Saturday skies above the marsh with their teary glow. The uplit mushrooms at Stratford's new bus station, planted just across the road from the shopping centre where my mum used to work, now mingle with drifting clouds in the oblique glass wall of the new Jubilee Line ticket hall; and, beyond them, the Central Line rises from its burrow beside a vast Sahara of gravel and slag that one day, they say, will be a velodrome, a running track, a swimming pool.

I grew up around here.

Passing the site of Lea Bridge station

PHOSPHORUS MATT HAYNES

THE YEAR OF THE STRIKE was the year I died. 1888, I was sixteen, and already used to the iron taste of spit in my mouth, but when I lost my first tooth, I cried. Then one day my boy Tom said, "Annie, I can see your bones, it's like there's a candle inside you" – and it was true: I glowed in the dark, like a ghost, like a ghost…

From the factory tower on Sundays I watched my father fishing, growing old without me. And I watched my little brother's children, George and Samuel, the nephews whose cheeks I'd never kiss, walk beside him on the path to Marshgate Lane, where Sam, who came home from Passchendaele, built his first print works. Last week, after the diggers moved in, the old enamel sign stuck out of the earth like a flag or a bone on a battlefield: *Samuel Seares & Sons.*

At night now I drift through smart new flats where us girls used to lick the white phosphorus. That sudden flare in the corner of your eye, like someone has just struck a match –

Did I make you jump?

THE RINGERS

MARK SADLER

THE MINI-SUPERMARKET ON WHALERS ROW used to be a short hop down the road from where I live. Recently, the family who own it won a victory in court overturning an enforced purchase and demolition order. It is now the only permanent structure still standing on the site of the Olympic Park.

Since the construction crews moved in and barricaded the area behind wooden hoardings, getting to it has become more complicated. I have to go the long way around and enter the site via a temporary gate at the far end of Sea Alley, one of three surviving tidal streets in the capital – it still floods twice daily to a depth of around two feet. The buildings along there have raised doorways made accessible by a contiguous stone staircase whose uppermost tier functions as a narrow pavement when the tide is in. There used to be a hot-water bottle factory that backed on to it. I worked there for a couple of months after I left school.

After you pass through the gate at the end of Sea Alley, you are walking on what will eventually be the Olympic Park. At the moment, there's nothing much there beyond the broken concrete foundations of former buildings, scraped clean by the roaming bulldozers. A makeshift footpath through the rubble, roughly a quarter of a mile in length, has been marked out by two continuous ribbons of ragged yellow tape, looped intermittently around rusting iron posts.

The supermarket was once part of a long terrace. Remnants of brickwork belonging to the adjoining properties still cling to the side walls at points where its removal might compromise the surviving structure.

After three decades of being on nodding terms with the family who run the place, I finally spoke properly to the current owner a few days ago. He told me that the name of the shop (which is spelled out in Arabic characters on the yellow sign above the door) is "International Bazaar".

Although we both grew up in the area, we went to different schools. As we conversed, I wondered whether he recalled the torrents of racial abuse that my classmates and I would shout at him and his younger brother in the street as they walked home together. In all the years that I've visited the shop he has never shown any traces of animosity towards me. Maybe I am giving myself and my actions too much credit. I was just one of many: a forgettable face loitering somewhere on the margins of an ugly crowd. It's possible that he doesn't remember me, or perhaps he chooses not to.

Back then, he seemed like a bright lad, always very smartly turned out. He carried a shiny black leather satchel-briefcase to and from school. It smacked of ambition and upward mobility, and made us all hate him even more. I took it for granted that he'd grow up to be a doctor or a lawyer, and that the evening shifts he put in at his parents' shop were just a stopgap on his way to a better life. It never occurred to me that, almost thirty years later, he'd still be here, rooted firmly on the spot, ringing up my purchases.

"How long do you think you'll be able to hang on here?" I asked him.

"It's getting harder now. Deliveries are a problem." He stacked six identical tins of chicken soup neatly in the bottom of the thin blue carrier before placing the paper bag of rambutans on top. "You understand that my family have been here a long time. This is our home. My parents built this business up from nothing. It's not only about money. There is a principle at stake."

The tarnished gold, silver and bronze coins that I handed to him seemed like an ominous portent of what was to come.

Next door to the International Bazaar there used to be an independent chemist's called Dusky's. The proprietor was a man named Robert Dusky. He was the descendent of a Lascar who had jumped ship at East India Docks and settled in east London. A gilt-framed, poster-sized daguerreotype of his nautical ancestor, dressed in ceremonial sailors' garb, hung on the wall behind the counter.

Mr Dusky made his own cough syrup from ingredients that he grew in a sunken barge on the River Lea. He never kept his medicine out on display in the shop but, if you asked, there was always a plentiful supply in the back room. They raised the barge from the river a few weeks ago. It was early one morning. I could hear the sound of the crane and smell the thick diesel fumes drifting into my tiny bathroom through the open window. The badly corroded hull was suspended in the cold spring air behind the wooden hoardings that screened off the construction site. A tangle of overgrown river plants trailed over the sides, their poorly distributed weight causing the boat to tilt upwards slightly at one end. A panicked moorhen that had become trapped in the stagnant morass of slimy roots and branches squawked and flapped in a vain attempt to free itself.

I sat down on the lid of the toilet in my underwear and attempted to manhandle my wet feet into a pair of shrunken socks. The bone-dry elastic made a strained tearing sound as I wrestled the material over my heels. After I had finished dressing, I looked out of the window again. The barge was still dangling from the mast of the crane, which now seemed paralysed with indecision. The moorhen's struggles had ceased with its cries, which had become increasingly plaintive and high-pitched before they stopped. Its body hung motionless in the weeds.

Dusky's cough syrup was a transparent pale pink liquid with the consistency of thick honey and a peculiar floral taste. The Lea Valley Rose petals that were suspended in the mixture made a slow, downward migration from the neck of the bottle that could take months. When the last one reached the bottom you were meant to throw the bottle away.

My mum used to give it to me when I was sick. When I was a bit older, I shared a bottle with a girl called Karen. We lay in bed, watching *The Sullivans* on the black and white portable television, the pair of us struck dumb by a spreading inner warmth that made it feel like everything was happening underwater and in slow motion. If you drank more than a bottle in one go it would start to affect your time perception. Events would break down to a series of snapshots, as if somebody was depressing the fast-forward button on the video cassette of your life and pausing at random moments. I would suddenly become aware that I was standing at the bar of The King's Beacon with a beer in my hand and no recollection of how I'd got there. A second later, I'd be on the top deck of a bus. Then I'd be at home, or at another pub, or splayed out in the fire exit of the bingo hall with my legs, protruding from the tiled alcove, stretched halfway across the pavement.

There was a punk club called Nell's that I used to frequent in Woolwich. It was held every Wednesday in the cellar of The Cannons. One night in October, 1980, I downed two bottles of Dusky's in the toilets. I awoke the following evening, fully dressed. My shirt was torn and covered in blood. A partial reddish-brown body print marked the wall of my bedroom, as if I had charged into it with my arms spread wide open, like a cartoon character who has been fooled into thinking that he can pass through a solid object. I went to the bathroom to check myself in the mirror. There were rose petals stuck to my face. My mate Nigel, who was at Nell's that night, never spoke to me again. When I asked Kevin, who was also there, what had happened, he told me that there was no point going over it and that I should keep schtum.

It wasn't until a few days later that I read about the murders in the free paper. A scuffle had broken out down at the front while Bible Dick were playing. Two girls had had their throats slashed open with a broken bottle. They bled to death at the foot of the stage with Richard Sandford towering over them in his leather trousers, glowering at the audience like a mad Roman emperor presiding over an execution carried out in his honour. Of course, I don't remember any of that.

For weeks afterwards, I would almost jump out of my skin every time somebody knocked on the front door. In the end, though, it was Steven Burrell who was arrested and, following a solid eighteen hours of interrogation, confessed to the killings. By this point in his life he had already had run-ins with the law. People had started calling him "Psycho Burrell" and so no one was surprised when he was charged. If he hadn't been sent down for that, then it would have been for something else. He was barely seventeen when they locked him up. They let him out four years ago. A few months later I bumped into his old mum working behind the bar at The Swan. I asked her how he was coping with being back on the road. She told me that he was finding it hard to adjust. What can you say to that? He went in there a boy and came out nearly middle-aged, one year shy of his fortieth birthday. There are things that you're supposed to do with your life in those decades that he never had the opportunity to do. You can never get any of that lost time back. There's a point when you're so far behind you can never catch up. It's too late.

I asked her for his address and promised that I'd look in on him.

"Best not," she said quietly as she laid my change down on one of the wet bar towels.

———————————

Growing up, Steven and I were both thugs. The only difference between us was that he was a leader and I was a follower. He had natural charisma. People looked up to him and took their cue from him. Even though we never talked about it, I know where his anger came from, because we shared the same experience.

It happened in the toy shop on the corner of Whalers Row and Davis Straight, although the seeds were sown a few years before I ever set foot in the place. When I think back on it now it seems to me that my future was predetermined. That the events leading up to what was to occur were so meticulously ordered and so carefully set in motion that there was simply no alternative. It was as if my fate lay at the end of a column of upright pub dominoes that had passed through many hands and would inevitably fall in line towards a pre-selected point after the first one was toppled.

My granddad was dying from bowel cancer. My mum moved him into our flat so that she could look after him. He slept in my room. I moved onto the settee. When Mum was working night shifts at the hospital he used to get out of bed and sit in front of the TV in his cigarette-burned pyjamas, drinking cans of Hofmeister and telling me stories about the war.

My favourite tale was about a night in December during the Blitz when the Luftwaffe dropped thousands of tin soldiers onto east London. My granddad was in the Anderson shelter at the bottom of his garden with the rest of his family, bracing himself for the explosions. But all that he could hear over the drone of the bombers was a sound like nuts and bolts raining down on the corrugated-iron roof. In the morning, there were all these toy soldiers scattered everywhere – "as if we'd accidentally shot down Father Christmas," he said. People were cleaning them out of their drains and gutters. You would find them in bushes and trees, woven into the superstructure of old crows' nests, or submerged in the powdery silt at the bottom of garden ponds. There was a stigma about collecting them because they were models of German infantry, and also because of the rumours going around that they had been cast from metal salvaged from British planes that had been shot down over Europe.

The toy shop on Whalers Row was run by a man called Mr Lord. He owned a Rolls Royce and always dressed like he was on his way to meet the Queen. His conspicuous wealth made him stand out, but he had a knack of getting along with people of all stripes and was a respected figure in the community. Prior to his arrival on the row, the shop had been the Neng brothers' hardware store and had done very good business.

Mr Lord had amassed a very large collection of these German toy soldiers. Once you got to know him, he would get some of them out on the glass counter top so that you could have a good look at them. They were roughly a centimetre taller than normal toy soldiers. What I liked about them was the detail that had gone into their faces, which were frozen in bestial expressions of anger, hatred and battle lust. The rarest one was a model of Hitler firing a pistol side on, as if he was a participant in a duel. You could see that their purpose had been to create discord on the home front. The Germans didn't need to drop a real army onto London. They had their tin soldiers to stir in the hearts of children not just the unquenchable need to possess forbidden objects, but also the anxiety these objects engendered that somewhere across the English Channel was a race of fierce warrior giants who were capable of killing ten of our boys for every one of them that we managed to put down. It was the kind of neurosis and fear that spreads invisibly from the very young to the very old and makes adults, particularly parents, acutely aware of their own powerlessness. They were meant to break morale but in the end it didn't work. My granddad said that, after the initial shock wore off, everybody just got used to seeing them around.

I used to try to buy these soldiers from Mr Lord. I would lay all the money that I made from my paper round down on the counter and attempt to bargain with him. One day in the middle of our negotiations he walked over to the door and turned the key in the lock. He hung a cheery sign up in the window stating that he would be back in five minutes. We went behind the curtain at the back of the counter and into a bridging corridor between the front and the rear of the property. It was no more than three feet from one end to the other and was paved with flagstones that seemed to belong to an older incarnation of the building. The middle slab had a braided crack running along the centre of it. I stared at the crack with my head bowed like it was the only thing in the world, trembling as Mr Lord put his right hand down the front of my trousers and his other hand down his own.

When he was finished he wiped himself clean with the handkerchief that he kept in his waistcoat pocket. We both went back into the shop. He laid out a small selection of the soldiers on the counter and asked me to pick one. While I was doing this he unlocked the door and took the sign down. After he returned he took the soldier that I had chosen and put it into a pink and white candy-striped paper bag. He neatly folded over the top and gave it to me.

I was at the door when he called out:

"I expect that I'll see you again next week, Jason."

When I didn't answer him he added:

"It would be a shame if I had to go to the police and tell them that you'd been stealing from me."

I don't know why I kept going back there but I did. Because I don't understand, I can't make peace with it or with myself. At one time I had forty-one of those soldiers in my late granddad's tobacco tin under my bed. I couldn't bear to play with them, but I couldn't bring myself to throw them away either. The bailiffs took them in the end, but that wasn't until years later after I lost my job and moved back in with my mum. There was this boy at my school called Phillip Rag. He was a year below me. He had some of the soldiers too. I knew where he'd got them from because there was only one source. He used to show off his own collection in the playground. I fucking hated him. Once I caught him trading a German SS officer for a Mars bar. I beat the shit out of him that day and he never knew why. To him, it was just an ordinary, run-of-the-mill beating.

Steven was different to Phillip. You couldn't imagine him allowing anyone to take advantage. He would fight back. I'll never forget the afternoon I went over to his house with Louis Porter. There were about fifty of those toy soldiers on his windowsill. I could never look him in the eye after that.

There must have been a day, just an ordinary day, not long after the turn of the century, when somebody with wealth and influence looked down at a plan of east London and put a red line through Whalers Row as if it was an incorrect answer in a test. They made a decision that it wasn't worth keeping; that what had happened there wasn't worth remembering.

In time the street will be struck from the pages of the *A-to-Z*. Its foundations will be excised from the city, denied the opportunity to sink down into the earth and become part of London archaeology. A year from now the only tangible evidence of its existence will be a small sack of undeliverable letters in a Royal Mail sorting office.

In 2012 the Olympic Games will be staged here. They will fly ringers in from all over the world; people who can offer this corner of the capital a better, prouder legacy than any of us who grew up here ever could. The sprinters will crouch down on their starting blocks, near to where the International Bazaar currently stands. When the pistol fires they will propel themselves towards a fixed point, one hundred metres away, at speeds fast enough for them to break through the horizon and into the wider world beyond. I could never move fast enough, or with enough purpose or direction to escape the circumstances of my birth. I staggered punch-drunk into the walls of my bedroom like a trapped bluebottle smashing its head against plate glass. In Mr Lord's toy shop I stared passively at a crack in the flagstones that would never open wide enough to swallow me up. When the construction crews arrived and began to dig my foundations out from under me, I hung there like the dying moorhen caught in the overgrown tangle of Mr Dusky's underwater garden on the River Lea.

When Whalers Row is gone we will all be refugees; Londoners taken out of context. Our destiny is to be marginalised and, later, to be squeezed out of the picture altogether.

Olympic P[ ]
Construction Site

British Waterway and towpath closed
No entry beyond this point

These passageways are under
C.C.T.V surveillance

For further information contact
Construction Hotline 0800 072 2110

Waterborne emergencies contact
0800 47 999 47

CCTV

operates in this area to
increase public safety and
reduce/prevent crime.

Please contact the Olympic
Delivery Authority
at 0800 072 2110
for further information

"When we were kids, to push your way through the bushes and reach those overgrown channels of silent green water was to enter some sort of secret wonderland…"

Under Section 107 of the 1968 Transport Act, Channelsea River, City Mill River, Prescott Channel, Pudding Mill River, Abbey Creek, Three Mills Back River, Three Mills Wall River and Waterworks River were designated "remainder waterways"; they officially no longer served any useful purpose, and British Waterways' obligations to them were minimal: they could be revived, sold, or – if the economic argument was strong – simply eliminated.

As we drove home across the marshes, I'd see the factory
walls reflected in the green water of the canal and, with
a child's logic, think it not at all remarkable that the tiny
Hillman Imps and Ford Zodiacs in the box below my bed
should be made just down the road from where I lived.
When the name was sold, production moved to Macau,
and for years now the buildings have stood empty. High
above the windows, though, ghosts of fallen letters still
spell the words I remember: *Lesney "Matchbox" Toys.*

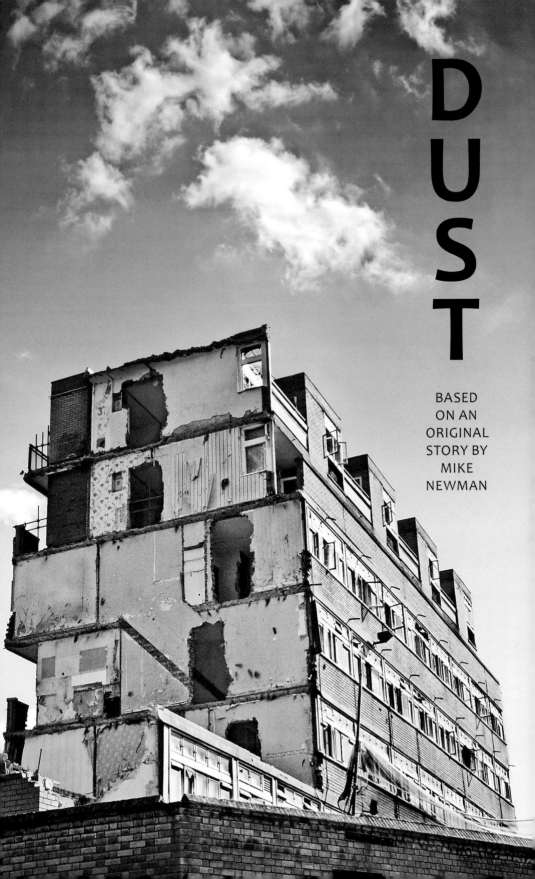

DUST

BASED
ON AN
ORIGINAL
STORY BY
MIKE
NEWMAN

LEWIS ZIPPED HIS LEATHER COAT UP TO HIS CHIN and buried his hands in the worn pockets. Then, moving swiftly, he crossed Cadogan Terrace and entered the park. Here were joggers, Saturday-morning strollers, confidential couples buried in gossip and domestic affairs, and lines of fitness seekers in numbered tops. Lewis grimaced. He wanted coffee, and recalled a friendly kiosk where several pathways met. But that meant lingering in the park, staying near the marshes.

If he pinched his fingers together he could still feel the cool wire of the detonator passing between them. Even in the damp, chill marsh air, he'd been able to twist the slender coil almost without thought – he'd done it often enough to know how brittle it could be, how it behaved in extreme heat or cold. He could also tell the good quality, expensive kit from the cheap Eastern European stuff dealt from the backs of the dusty white Transits pulled up against the blue fence. Lewis admired the efficiency of the gloomy men who hauled their gear out into the street then palmed the rolled wad of cash and disappeared. He wished he could stay so detached from his work. It too, after all, was a kind of theft.

He paused beside the cordoned-off fountain. He had to decide whether to head south towards the canal or north into the blur of Mare Street. The quiet of the canal appealed, but beside the calm water were stocky yellow town houses not unlike the ones from earlier. Their windows would bear fading Greenpeace stickers, their doorsteps would carry a cargo of charity collection bags and free newspapers, and wind chimes would hang silently in their porches. When no one was at home, it was easy to picture these houses as abandoned – a half-drunk cup of coffee on a work surface, a plastic tricycle tipped back in the yard. But then a child's cry, or a voice raised, would snap the scene to life. He turned north, out of the park.

As he walked, he found himself thinking once more about Montgomery House. He'd been a young man then, idealistic and keen. But, fifteen years on, memories of that bright blue afternoon in September were still as clear and vivid as the sky above the city had been in the seconds before the explosion. He closed his eyes and saw again that awkward scrap of concrete, pierced with steel rods, falling like a broken Sputnik out of the dust clouds; and, yards away across the grass, the woman who'd watched it fall towards her, spellbound. She shouldn't have been so close. It wasn't his fault she'd been so close.

On Mare Street, crowds of uniformed private schoolgirls milled at the bus stops, bitter at the prospect of Saturday-morning lessons.

They leered at him as he shuffled past, then, moments later, burst into muffled laughter.

Lewis sat by the window of the cafe, hunched over thick Turkish coffee. The waitress, bored and underemployed, watched him through yellow hair which swung in a tangle of extensions as she brushed the counter. There was a hint of bleach on the greasy air. Lewis needed places to be clean. He couldn't stomach dust. Sometimes in places like this he'd sweep a surreptitious finger along a shelf then raise it to his face. If his finger bore a film of dust, he'd never go back. Dust seemed to follow Lewis. It was in his clothes and in his hair. The stale taint of dust flattened Lewis's senses.

He reflected on the morning's work, wincing at how his hands had shaken, not with the chill of the marsh but – as always – with fear; the fear that people were still there. As he unrolled lengths of cable and placed charges, he would glimpse movement in hallways, or catch the glint of light on the face of a watch. He would wipe his feet when stepping from mud into the empty shell of a building, and peer around doors to avoid disturbing long-gone inhabitants.

The cafe owner appeared from some hidden back room, white shirt and apron stained and smeared. He yammered at the waitress, his voice cutting through the background babble of the radio, then gestured towards Lewis and his empty cup. Lewis slid from his seat, and headed out into the street.

The bus nosed past Dalston Lane. It had made slow progress through Hackney, slow enough for Lewis to read every word of resentful graffiti. *Regeneration is degeneration* he repeated under his breath; it was a refrain he'd heard protestors chanting on a site nearby. He was alone on the lower deck, and not really sure where he was headed.

That morning, after everything had gone quiet, after the hard-hatted workers had retreated beyond the tape cordon, after he'd checked the connections and depressed the switch on the small black box in his right hand and jabbed his left thumb onto the button, he'd seen – he was sure – a pale, frightened face at a window. But then the yellow bricks had tumbled, sucked into the space inside the houses, and the dust had risen.

And then, once the dust cloud had rolled away, a new horizon had appeared. Steel rods stuck from the rubble like fractured bones broken through skin. Only one house, the one at the end that connected to another empty block, still stood. But its rooms were ripped open, pale blue wallpaper flapping and torn, pictures still hanging on the walls of long-cold bedrooms. He'd turned away to pack up his bag, choosing not to hear the muttered appreciation: "Nice job, Lewis, man."

A few years back, this would have been an event – the whole community would have turned out to watch. Just like they had that bright blue afternoon when Montgomery House, a twenty-storey slab tower overlooking the Tyne, had come down. It had been like a carnival; people were having a day out in the sun, having fun. And, one year out of training, he'd stood in hard hat and high-vis tabard, watching them, amazed at how close they were allowed to stand.

The bus drew to a halt at the post office. The driver tore a receipt from the ticket machine, opened the doors, and glanced back down the saloon. Lewis sighed, and hauled himself out.

The entrance gates to Abney Park Cemetery loomed in front of him: *the gates of the abode of the mortal part of man*, no less, if the worn hieroglyphs on the Egyptian-revival pillars were to be believed. Lewis stepped through and walked between tall trees dripping moisture. Reaching a fallen headstone, he sat and rested his cheek on a marble angel. Conversation drifted across to him from a pale and plump American girl on some sort of gothic tour. She was declaring the place to be "awesome" and Lewis, though he would not have used that word, was inclined to agree.

Something one of the expert witnesses had said at the inquest had always stuck with Lewis: *distance is the best safeguard*.

Now, more than ever, he understood that.

DREAMWORLD

Juno Baker

ABOUT FIVE YEARS BEFORE IT ALL HAPPENED, I visited the Olympic site on a work team-building day.

Our guide explained how she'd run round to her neighbour's when she'd heard the Games were coming to London. The emotion choked her up. For her, it was a dream come true. For me, it was the stuff of nightmares: sweaty nylon shorts and sports mania wrapped up in a shell suit of banal corporate sponsorship. I stared out of the minibus window and tried not to hear.

Outside was Europe's largest construction site, dotted with tiny creatures in fluorescents and hard hats clenching their faces against the wind and rain as they worked. I watched the UK's biggest digger poking bricks out of a tower block; huge vehicles rumbling over the dirt on caterpillar tracks; giant machines swallowing up contaminated soil and spewing out clean, brown earth. I was still sulky about having the Games, but had to admit this was all pretty impressive.

As we drove on, it became other-worldly. We weren't in London any more; we were on some sort of moonscape, an eerie terrain where nothing grew but the flatness of the land and the length of the horizon. We turned a corner. Ahead, Victorian terraces, shops and a pub – its old sign swinging in the dust-filled breeze – sat empty, waiting for demolition. I wondered how many people had staggered out of that pub over the decades, how many bar brawls it had seen, and what they had been about.

After lunch, in a dark, wood-panelled room in the old town hall, we had a session with three excitable councillors. It was that time in the day when you wouldn't mind a little nap. But we had to listen to these three telling us all the great things the Olympics would bring to London: new homes, jobs and prosperity, waterways and swans. The Games would be an inspiration, and help to tackle gun crime:

"Young people with an interest in guns will watch the shooting events in Woolwich and see that you don't have to shoot *people* to have fun with a gun."

That roused me from my stupor.

I raised my hand. The department head looked uneasy. I don't remember exactly how I phrased it – innocuously enough, I think – but I had to check what sort of dreamworld this councillor was living in. Did she really think people join gangs because they want to have a go at shooting?

It turned out she did.

"My dad came over from Spanish Town in the fifties, and I got the allotment from him. As long as you dug your patch and kept it tidy, that's all that mattered. Some of the old guys teased him, but they meant nothing. There were all kinds here. One year, as a joke, he planted bananas – didn't tell them, just watched their eyes go like saucers when they saw the leaves. But folk used to grow everything. Grapes, they grew – Manor Gardens wine! Good stuff. When he left the buses my dad spent every day here, had his ashes scattered over by the shed. Built that himself out of old doors from the dump. They say they'll put it all back once it's over, but... how can you put back a hundred years?"

BEHIND THE BLUE DOORS

Rishi Dastidar

I BLAME *TIME OUT* MYSELF.

Not least among the things it's fashionable to accuse that once proudly fat, now slim, humbled and scant listings magazine of doing is allowing the degradation of itself into the freesheet all the other freesheets laugh at when they gather together at tube stations to be shoved at the bored and uninterested. But how many of those digests of the ephemeral, the unnecessary, the useless, have ever prompted you to do something that resulted in you being thrown off the Olympic Park?

Exactly.

Back in the day when the cliché "back in the day" was as freshly minted as a lamb wearing a herb titfer in the light spring rain, *Time Out* used to live up to its title by suggesting things to do that didn't involve a vague sense of existential disquiet at spending borrowed money in venues dedicated to separating you from cash, sobriety and self-worth: it suggested going on walks. Perambulations in and about the Wen and the greater Home Counties which, through a complicated algorithm involving the number of fields traversed, the uncomfortableness of your footwear, and the number of pubs you refreshed yourself at – all bracketed inside a complex Gore-Tex function – could make you into a better person, rather than the sort of undesirable who frequents "bars" and has a "lifestyle", whatever that might be.

And, five years ago, it was the memory of one of these improving promenades that prompted my co-conspirator to say: you know what, we should have a wander up the River Lea. And why ever not? Too rarely in life do we dare to confront the sheds of light industry full on, to inhale the air that is mostly particulates from fish cans and spark plugs and cement factories, to say: "Fuck you, West London, and all your mere shopping; this is how life *is*."

So it was that we found ourselves one Sunday high-tailing it through the try-harder vistas of Three Mills, a place now dedicated to the grinding down of talent and ambition into mere "media content", past the Lock-Keepers' Cottages where faded rock stars' molls, ginger milkmen and aliens once made us breakfast, and – with a shimmy off the obvious track and with the Blackwall Tunnel Northern Approach roaring away in our left ears – alongside barely rippling, bottle-green water and concrete banks dotted with waist-high weeds swaying in an almost-forgotten breeze. We stopped. In front of us was an underpass

slightly wider than the path by the river bank, blocked off by two wooden doors painted Dodger blue. On them was a sign in roadwork yellow, courtesy of Thames Water. *No Entry*, it said. *Works Here Until April*. Now it was August. And there was no padlock. The right-hand door was open; more than open – it had flung itself hard back against the supporting wall of the underpass.

What else to do? We walked on through.

As we emerged from the hundred yards or so of gloom, it seemed as if the sun had decided to say yes to this minor act of transgression, rewarding us with its first lazy beams of the day. We were now on the right-hand side of the river, strolling up what had the feel of a backlit studio lot, the walls of silent factories as impermanent as balsa wood cut-outs. Every second window was smashed. Those icons of the ending of the manufacturing age, pyramids of tyres, were plentiful, awaiting their ritual burning, tonight, tomorrow, forever. Some crows nestled on a wharf over the way, reminding us that they were the kings now.

A cyclist, angry for some reason, and looking like a fly with amputated wings, huffed past us, throwing back over his shoulder a question: did we know what was further up? We didn't, a response that elicited another huff and then an acceleration away from us.

We carried on, gambolling beside a river moving almost as fast. Gently we carried ourselves up and round a rising hairpin bend, until we had crested and landed on a road leading to, well, we couldn't quite see where. It was as silent and empty as a city could ever be.

Which was, presumably, why the Ford Fiesta pulled up alongside at that moment. Dirty, building-site white; its driver in hi-vis jacket, walkie-talkie worn proudly as badge. As he wound down his window, the last remnants of crackling conversation cut out.

"What are you doing here?" Always a strong opening gambit.

"We were just walking…" I faltered almost as quickly as I had started, confirming in his head that we must be guilty of *something*.

"You do know you're trespassing, right?"

Now an uneasy look passed between me and my co-conspirator who had, subtly, wisely, shuffled just those crucial few paces behind me.

"No, we didn't. There weren't any signs up or anything."

He considered this for a moment.

"Yeah, that's probably right. We haven't got round to doing them everywhere yet. Anyway, you're on the Olympic Park. So I'm going to have to escort you off now. Hop in."

Meekly, that's what we did, clambering into the back of the car with no thought of protest crystallising in our slightly bewildered minds.

The journey down to the exit – not a long trip, it can't have been more than a minute or so – was silent, bar one interjection from the driver. Jerking his head to the left, he said: "The stadium'll be over there."

Gliding towards the traffic gates which would become the main entrance, we were startled most by the moonscape aspect the Park had already acquired: flat greys made duller by the clean, primary brightness of all the diggers and the trucks revelling in what they knew would be the best playground available to them for years. As we were deposited at Pudding Mill Lane station – with an unexpectedly cheery wave and a smile from the man who had nabbed us – we were already composing the structure of the anecdote that was to become *The One About Us Being Thrown Off The Olympic Park.*

We have been back behind that blue fence since, but once only, and as fully paying guests this time. And while it was all wonderful in that way we must say it was, whatever we might really feel, the thing that really was wonderful was the meadow of wild flowers that had been planted down by the Lea where it sludgily wrapped its arms around the now-real stadium. However transplanted, however fake, they were a memory, an echo, of what was previously there; making a claim, saying: *yes, you might be here now, temporary carnival of commercial sports; but we will be back, because that is how life is.*

In the summer of 2011, as a test run for the Olympics,
trial equestrian events were held in Greenwich Park.
Large areas of grass were cordoned off, access to the
Observatory restricted, and small tents provided
in which the horses could get changed.

An Altercation at the Gate

Matt Haynes

Greenwich Park, Maze Hill Gate. The path leading to the Observatory is blocked by a metal fence. Just inside the fence is a tent with a pointed roof; it is somewhat medieval in appearance, and rather reminiscent of those once used in jousting tournaments. Just outside the fence is a SECURITY GUARD; *he is talking to a young and, it has to be said, rather* HANDSOME PHOTOGRAPHER.

SECURITY GUARD: Could you not do that, sir.

HANDSOME PHOTOGRAPHER: Sorry?

SECURITY GUARD: Could you not take photos.

HANDSOME PHOTOGRAPHER: Oh. *[He pauses.]* Why?

SECURITY GUARD: It's a temporary structure. They don't want people taking photos of the temporary structures.

HANDSOME PHOTOGRAPHER: I can't take a photo because it's temporary?

SECURITY GUARD: You can take a photo when it's gone.

HANDSOME PHOTOGRAPHER: But then it won't be there.

SECURITY GUARD:

HANDSOME PHOTOGRAPHER: Will it?

SECURITY GUARD:

HANDSOME PHOTOGRAPHER: Hello?

Exit, pursued by a squirrel.

Empire Villa

289 Westcombe Park Avenue
Greenwich
Tel: GRE 0978

The Editor
Greenwich Time

28th June, 2011

Sir,

My wife Mary and I are accustomed to taking our
"afternoon constitutional" in Greenwich Park, but
have lately found ourselves somewhat perturbed
by the state of the grass. Only last week I
remarked to Mary that it was looking distinctly
"worse for wear", and she said she was inclined
to agree with me. I was, therefore, extremely
pleased today to see large areas being fenced off
in order to let the "noble sod" grow back. Sadly,
many of our fellow "park-lovers" do not seem
to share my view. Indeed, Mary and I witnessed
several of them involved in angry conversations
with those employed to guard the fences. I would,
therefore, like to take advantage of your pages
to express my approval of what is being done, and
to encourage my fellow "Greenwichians" to think a
little more "long-term".

I remain, Sir, yrs etc.

Col. Gerald P. Cablecar (ret'd)

Empire Villa
289 Westcombe Park Avenue
Greenwich
Tel: GRE 0978

The Editor
Greenwich Time

5th July, 2011

Sir,

Many thanks for printing my letter in last week's edition of "Greenwich Time". When, however, I showed it to my wife, Mary, she pointed out that I was a "bloody fool". Having now had time to consider, I am inclined to agree with her, and would like to take advantage of your pages to clarify the matter.

I remain, Sir, yrs etc.

Gerald P. Cablecar.

Col. Gerald P. Cablecar (ret'd)

AS THEY STOOD THERE waiting to cross Greenwich High Road, a coach with a printed placard on its windscreen saying *Equestrian Shuttle* attempted to make a sharp right turn up Stockwell Street, and failed. It slumped to a halt, engine silent, awkwardly skewed across the junction just in front of them. In the window by the passenger door was a brightly coloured poster. It said that after 9 a.m. they could ride any bus in Northampton for just £3.75, and should ask the driver for details.

"Probably not the right moment," said Alex, as behind them a 180 sounded its horn, eager to be off to Belvedere Industrial Estate.

"I guess not," said Chris, "though I'd love to know more. I mean, it's a great offer, but... a pretty weird sort of add-on to dressage. Especially dressage in Greenwich."

"Maybe," said Alex, "after you've seen your twentieth camp stallion do the turkey trot and soft-shoe shuffle, a visit to the former home of the UK boot industry actually starts to sound rather enticing, and an all-inclusive ticket giving access to both the horses AND the entirety of Northampton's bus network a bit of a bargain?"

"It's a shame we can't ask him, but, as you say..."

"... probably not a good time."

THE NORTHANTS SOFT-SHOE SHUTTLE BUS

WHEN *GREENWICH TIME* REPORTER Arianne Hoover got in touch to say that she'd like to write a piece about the pedalo pond, we were intrigued, and asked her to tell us more. It turned out the pond had been requisitioned for use as a water jump on the cross-country course; it would be cleaned and landscaped, and a fish and a turtle introduced to add interest. Arianne's chief concern, though, was this: did anyone *really* think that horses enjoyed jumping from a height of several feet onto solid concrete, however cunningly disguised it was by a gravel veneer and two inches of water? Sensing yet more scandal – complaints were already circulating about how few tickets for the impending events seemed to have gone to SE10 residents in the recent appease-the-locals ballot – we gave her the nod; and also a small sub to cover expenses.

The first thing Arianne ascertained was that many people did indeed hold this view. The second was that they were mostly the same people who think there's little a crippled fox enjoys more than being chased ten miles across Leicestershire by red-faced men in jodhpurs and a pack of overexcited attack dogs. And the third thing was that she really couldn't face talking to people like that. So, being a professional, and not wishing to let us down, she interviewed the fish and the turtle instead.

MH

ARIANNE: So, you two – when were you introduced?

FISH: Oh, ages ago. There was this party, I'd been drinking like a...

ARIANNE: No, that's not what – oh, never mind. How come the pair of you were chosen for this great honour?

FISH: Well, it was all done by ballot.

TURTLE: Hundreds of us applied.

FISH: Thousands, I think. Everyone wanted to be involved.

TURTLE: Yes, you're probably right. Thousands.

ARIANNE: So... they just drew you out of a hat?

FISH: No, a jam jar. Why on earth would I be in a hat? And you were in a shoebox, weren't you, done up in straw?

TURTLE: That's right. They thought I was a tortoise.

FISH: Oh. And are you... not?

TURTLE: No.

FISH stares at TURTLE.

ARIANNE: Soooo... moving on... it's just the two of you?

FISH: Yes, that surprised us too. We assumed there'd be loads of us, given how many applied, but – no. Just me and him.

TURTLE: Her.

TURTLE stares at FISH.

FISH: Really?

TURTLE: Yes.

FISH stares at TURTLE.

FISH: Gosh. Anyway... yes, it's just the two of us. But that's fine.

TURTLE: It's actually lovely and peaceful... very very peaceful...

FISH: Yes. Peaceful. That is *definitely* the word. Full of... peace.

TURTLE: I mean, every so often a horse jumps on our heads, but...

FISH: *[laughing]* ... I think that happened to me last Saturday night at the Gate Clock too...

ARIANNE: The Ga... that's the Wetherspoons by the station, yes?

FISH: ... or at least that's how it felt next morning!

TURTLE stares at FISH.

TURTLE: You went to Wetherspoons? On Saturday? Without me?

FISH: Oh, so now I'm not allowed to have other friends, is that it? God, this is Barnes Wetland Centre all over again...

ARIANNE: I think, maybe, I should just... um... leave you to it...

..........GREENWICH TOWN CENTRE........

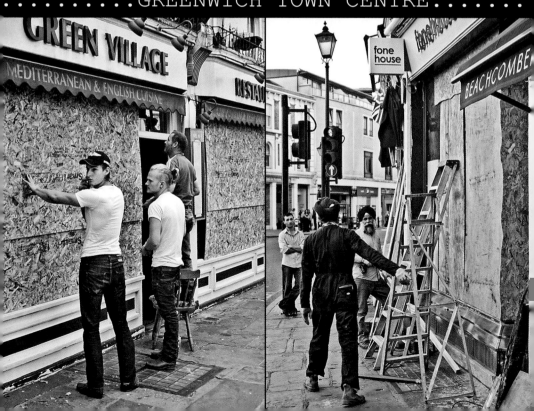

INTERNATIONAL HORSE ADVISOR

MATT HAYNES

SAY "EQUUS" TO MOST PEOPLE and they'll immediately think of Sidney Lumet's 1977 film about a teenage stable boy whose religiously inspired sexual fascination with horses culminates in an extended full-frontal nude scene with Jenny Agutter, as most things did in the mid-seventies. But it turns out that *Equus* is also the name of an American magazine for people who love horses in quite a different way. I know this because yesterday I had an anxious email from Jan, one of its columnists, asking for advice. Riders coming to Greenwich for the Olympics have been hearing reports of our riots, it seems, and started getting jittery. Is it, they want to know, still safe to splash out on those stars-and-stripes jodhpurs? How does Greenwich town centre compare to, say, downtown Detroit during a power outage? Should they – deep breath – tool up?

Truly, the internet is an extraordinary thing; one moment I'm cheerily tagging photos with the words "Greenwich riots", and the next I'm Official Advisor to the US Equestrian Team on the likelihood of anything occurring here next summer that might – and here again I'm forced to recall Miss Agutter's energetic performance amid the dimly lit hay bales – frighten the horses.

Greenwich was, indeed, like a ghost town last week, with chipboard offcuts swathing every shop around the market bar Greggs, which had – whether following a directive from head office, or simply using its own initiative, I don't know – chosen to pile the interior of its window with stacked packs of finger rolls, like miniature sandbags. Those people that *were* still about, though, seemed positively jolly: shopkeepers, policemen, men up stepladders with cordless drills, baffled tourists – all stood happily chatting and laughing at the absurdity of the situation. It was really quite heart-warming, as long as you didn't want to buy some garish Converse or a have a kebab.

What to say to Jan, though? As a resident of Greenwich, I want to tell her not to be silly, that it's just mountains and molehills. But, as a resident of the UK, I'd quite like us to tonk the Yanks.

I shall ponder.

But if Zara Phillips and the gang triumph narrowly over their American rivals next summer, and the US team tries to blame their steeds' sluggish trot and lack of height over the fences on the weight of the chain mail and the difficulty of maintaining balance whilst gripping a fifteen-foot lance in one hand and a mace in the other, then...

... you'll know the reason: they didn't like what they'd heard about the Big Society, and had decided not to take any chances.

A102(M)

MATT HAYNES

"Are we getting off at this blue one?" says the small boy standing unsteadily in the space between the front seats, nose pressed hard against the rain-wetted glass of the emergency door.

"No," says his father.

"Why not?"

"Because it's not our stop."

The train pulls into the platform at Bow Church. The boy stares down the track ahead.

"Where are we going, Daddy?"

"We're going where this train is going."

As the doors shut and the train accelerates away from the station, the boy's father holds the palm of his hand six inches behind his son's back. The same conversation, almost word for word, has occurred at Devons Road, Langdon Park and All Saints (for Chrisp Street Market). Soon, almost certainly, it will occur at Pudding Mill Lane.

"Choo choo," says the boy.

"Choo choo," murmurs his father.

The single track rises and curves east to run alongside the main line from Liverpool Street. The boy's father points out the Olympic Stadium, the tangled red loops of the ArcelorMittal Orbit, and the swooping concrete roof of Zaha Hadid's Aquatics Centre. His son stares through the opposite window, clearly distracted by something.

"There's a motorway," he says.

His father follows his gaze. Ahead of them the track divides, sending trains either side of the single platform at Pudding Mill Lane.

"Are we getting off at this blue one?"

His father reflects for a moment.

"Actually," he says, "it's an A-road."

To Let

Short Term
Olympic Rental

07858-190030
www.AskJohnLaurence.com

A LANDMARK DEVELOP
INCORPORATING ONE,
THREE BEDROOM APA
FOR SHARED OWNER

0808 118 4308
www.genesishor
WWW.STRATFORDHALO.COM

Excerpts from a speech made by
Councillor Colin Foote-Tunnel to a meeting of
Greenwich Council, Monday, 7th November 2011

Stenographer: Matt Haynes

Before addressing the matter of the bins,
I would like to draw the meeting's attention
to the shocking scenes that took place on
Saturday in Greenwich and Blackheath.

I'm sure I'm not alone in wondering why,
at a time of day which can only be described
as "night", more than 100,000 people were
not only allowed to make their own way from
houses, pubs and bus stops to a large expanse
of unfenced and unlit grass, but also to
repeat this act of initiative when leaving
afterwards, despite many by that stage
being in a highly emotional state, having
just observed the licensed pyrotechnics and
possibly purchased a bacon bap from the
Blackheath Tea Hut (which, I might add in
parentheses, remained open throughout the
proceedings, despite having no bouncers from
a council-approved body on hand to supervise
queueing, no trained first-aid staff,
and no information point with multilingual
brochures).

Approximately fifteen minutes after the launch
of the final firework, I myself personally
observed that crowds on Croom's Hill were so
thick that cars attempting to drive up or
down the road - which, in what would appear
to be another inexplicable and potentially
lethal oversight, had NOT been closed off
since midday with all parking bays suspended
and traffic diverted via Creek Road, Deptford

Church Street and the Catford gyratory -
were forced to proceed very slowly, possibly
even in first gear, in order to avoid hitting
people.

Remarkably, some participants in what can
only be described as this high-spirited and
chaotic melee had chosen to bring children
with them, some clearly under the age of
sixteen. With no stewards present to warn
them of the obvious risks, many of these
youngsters were recklessly writing their names
in the air with sparklers. Others, too young
to walk, were being pushed in what can only
be described as pushchairs. I find it barely
credible that no one, at any stage, thought
to commission a thorough survey of Croom's
Hill, preferably with computer modelling,
or to hold a properly publicised public
meeting about the short-term repurposing of
the road; if they had, they would, I'm sure,
have quickly been made aware that Croom's
Hill contains several speed bumps which,
if not flattened or cordoned off, could cause
a small child on wheels to temporarily lose
control of its Mousey and/or Igglepiggle,
with potentially catastrophic consequences.

I do not, as you know, like to use phrases
such as "free-for-all" lightly but, as I
passed Greenwich Theatre, it was obvious that
the neighbouring Rose and Crown public house
was full of people enjoying a spontaneous
drink. No security staff were present, no
safety railings were in place for those who
chose to smoke outside, and no one wishing to
enter in a wheelchair would have been able to
do so without someone holding the door open
for them. Similar scenes could be observed
further on at the Mitre, and I've since heard

reports of people enjoying extemporaneous drinks in pubs of their own choosing all over Greenwich, Blackheath and Deptford.

I am now clear in my own mind that the events of last Saturday should be a wake-up call, as it is absolutely imperative that there be no repetition of these shamefully shambolic and dangerous scenes during next year's Olympic Games, when the eyes of the world will be upon us. While the Games are in progress - and let us not forget that up to 65,000 people may be trying to get into Greenwich Park in broad daylight through purpose-built entrance gates - it is essential that, at the very least, all stations and bus stops in the town centre be closed and all spectators driven to the arena in specially adapted minibuses from holding pens behind North Greenwich station, where they can be efficiently checked for suitable footwear, provided with protective helmets, given some Kendal mint cake and a whistle, and then allocated their own personal marshal who will escort them to their seat and buy them a soft drink and a choc ice, provided they have a signed letter from their GP confirming that it's OK for them to eat dairy. In addition, my 16-year-old son thinks it would be "really cool" if a 15-foot horse made out of strips of purple vinyl was stuck to a wall behind Greenwich station; I'm not entirely sure why, but I think it's important that we listen to what young people have to say. He thinks it should glow in the dark, but I'm not sure if this will be possible.

It's not too late for this still to be an enjoyable and fun experience for all the family.

JANUARY 2012

SO, TRONDHEIM...

MATT HAYNES

SNOW DOES PECULIAR THINGS TO PEOPLE. Suddenly, parents who've previously ruined perfectly pleasant dinner parties by expounding belligerently on the moral failings of those who let a child walk five minutes to school unaccompanied are gaily lashing their toddler to a tea tray and launching it down an icy slope across which burly thirty-year-olds with helmet cams are already hurtling on snowboards.

To one brought up on the broad majestic flood plain of the Lea, the sheer abundance of tobogganists out on the slopes in Greenwich Park yesterday was astonishing: almost everyone in SE10, it seems, has not just an atavistic urge to hurtle downhill at the first sign of the white stuff in their genes, but also a brightly coloured plastic luge in their understairs cupboard.

Seriously, hats off to you people. Though not literally, as it's bloody freezing.

And, as we sat in the Plume of Feathers afterwards, enjoying a Sunday roast and a few pints of Harvey's, our thoughts turned to whether, once all the horsey stuff was over, Greenwich could harness this passion for the powder and piste and go head to snow-goggled head with Albertville, Calgary or Trondheim in a bid for the 2022 Winter Olympics. It would, of course, take more to impress the IOC than a quick Alpine-themed makeover for the Blackheath Tea Hut – banning the bikers, installing a log fire, generally giving it more of an *après-ski* ambience and less of an *avant-cutlery* one – but… the sooner we get our chestnuts in the fire, so to speak, the better.

Still musing on this, we trotted off to the Old Royal Naval College to get ourselves embroidered on History's Rich Tapestry (I'm afraid I often get embroidered after a few pints of Harvey's) by witnessing Greenwich's official pre-Olympic gaining of the royal imprimatur, just like we were Tunbridge Wells or Berkshire or a packet of overpriced biscuits. And, while the PA broadcast Side One of the mayor's well-worn copy of *Now That's What I Call Nationalistic Volume 35* (Thomas Arne's *Rule, Britannia!*, Elgar's *Pomp and Circumstance*, Blake's *Jerusalem*, Skrewdriver's *White Power / Smash the IRA*… all the classics…) and fireworks lit the sky, I took it upon myself to tell shivering knots of bemused foreign tourists that this was something we did every Sunday evening in Greenwich – got together by the river and listened to patriotic music whilst watching fireworks.

Because that sort of thing plays well with the IOC.

So, come on, Trondheim – what you got?

ARE YOU CONCERNED ABOUT WHAT IS HAPPENING IN GREENWICH PARK?

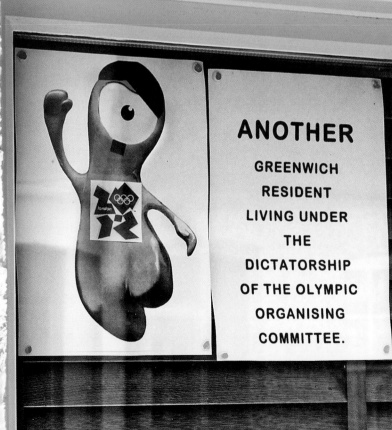

I wonder if anyone can help me. I really need to buy a hat for my dog, but I can't find anywhere that sells them. Does anyone know where I can buy a hat for my dog? #doghat
Expand

 GOAWAY @leaveusalone   46m
Woolwich #Olympics shooting venue: building contract was given to company based in deep-dyed Irish republican Cork, Ireland (not in the UK).
Expand

 GOAWAY @leaveusalone   45m
Woolwich #Olympics shooting venue: given the resurgent threat on UK mainland of Irish terrorism, is not the contractor I would have chosen.
Expand

 GOAWAY @leaveusalone   42m
Woolwich #Olympics shooting venue: there is a terrible "history" between Irish republican terrorism and Woolwich. #KingsArms 7 November 1974
Expand

 GOAWAY @leaveusalone   28m
Woolwich #Olympics shooting venue: If LOCOG's "Irish" ballistic screen does not stop lead shot, many acres/ground water will be contaminated
Expand

Are you terrified by the thought of not being able to park directly outside your house for a couple of weeks?

Are you disgusted that you won't be allowed to walk in the park whenever you want, because other people are enjoying themselves at a one-off event?

Are you confused by the concept of perspective?

Are you seriously saying that a contractor based in Cork shouldn't be allowed to work on the Woolwich site because the IRA bombed the King's Arms in 1974?

Are you? Really?

Are you having trouble with your line spacing?

The Twitter name and profile picture have been changed.
The tweets are real. Other than the one about the dog hat, obviously.

VICTORIA WOOD AND

Another week, another letter from the council. This one comes from Victoria Wood. Not that Victoria Wood, sadly, but her namesake in (deep breath) Development Control at the Directorate of Regeneration, Enterprise and Skills – I've no idea what that is, but I'm guessing it's where Greenwich Council stores all its recently repossessed nouns. Anyway; Victoria wants to inform me, sadly not through the medium of comic song, that I have 21 days to object to the erection of a temporary sign, 15 foot by 15 foot, round the back of Greenwich station.

It is, suffice to say, the first I've heard of this. And usually when a woman draws your attention to a large and unexpected temporary erection, your best bet is to smile awkwardly and shuffle behind the sofa; unless you're at a party and she's simply trying to break the ice, in which case suggesting she finds a steak mallet or small hammer generally makes more sense. Clearly, though, neither response is appropriate here. But what is? Vicky's letter really doesn't give me too much to go on, and my immediate thought is that we're about to get something like…

THE BIG PURPLE HORSE

Or maybe something more parochial. Maybe every street in SE10 is to be blessed with a towering billboard image of Chris Roberts, Leader of Greenwich Council, beaming into the middle distance as, like poor put-upon peons in Pyongyang, we scurry beneath his beneficent gaze and marvel at the greatness of his works.

Clearly, I need to find out more about Planning Application 12/0971/A. Which means either a trip to Woolwich Library, or going online. And last time I went to Woolwich I got chased by a man with very little hair and a very angry dog, eager to discuss their right to walk on a designated cycle path when there was a perfectly good pedestrian walkway alongside, so just hold on a moment while I boot up.

Aha.

OK... I've gone online... and I've found a mock-up... and it seems we're going to get a horse... a big horse sketched out on the exterior brickwork below Platform 1 in adhesive strips of purple vinyl. And not illuminated. On this particular point, the application is very clear: it will be non-illuminated signage. Basically, a 15-foot purple horse, stuck to a wall.

You know the sort of thing.

The thinking appears to be that Olympic spectators, being just a few mutations up the evolutionary ladder from deep-sea sponges, aren't capable of finding their way from Greenwich station to Greenwich Park without a 15-foot purple horse to guide them. Personally, I think that Olympic spectators should just look at a map; or, if they can't be bothered doing that, have their tickets confiscated. But there you go – that's just another difference between me and Seb Coe. I'm beginning to think the only thing we have in common is our profound love of German Expressionist cinema.

I don't think I'm going to object, though. Instead, I think I'll just write to Ms Wood to suggest that drug testing be extended from the athletes to all those who, when invited to brainstorm, begin gabbling about giant purple horses, and whether or not they should glow...

MATT HAYNES

WHITE POST LANE

TEMPLE MILL LANE

EASTWAY

NO PASARÁN!

Syd Bolton

With only a few weeks to Day Zero, all seems quiet on the Eastern Front, out on the hard shoulder of the A12, the Blackwall Tunnel Northern Approach. But back down the Commercial Road on this bitingly cold May morning, back past the Egyptian-Gothic splendour of the Star of the East, red and green Ampelmen, stranded on a poplared island, blink in the watery spring light. *They shall not cross!* Seventy-five years ago, just near here on Cable Street, thousands held the line against Mosley's Blackshirts; now, Olympic road closures are in place to allow another Fascist invention, the eternal flame, to pass freely.

Beyond Billingsgate's big yellow fish shed rise empty ten-grand-a-week rabbit hutches, built cheap, stacked high, and clad in primary-school-building-block colours. Short Olympic rental at get-rich-quick prices. The Wild East gold rush is under way. Minimum-wage workers with shiny hologrammed points-based visas put finishing touches to freshly painted railings, and to new tarmac smoothing-iron flat with not an exhaust-wrecking road hump or collapsed sewer in sight. Topiaried plastic hedgerows, hand-washed gravel walkways – what next? Letters to local residents, spelling out the etiquette for the welcoming party, getting us ready to receive our guests at the Great East End Knees-Up? Posters on every corner – *Your Country Needs You (To Behave)*?

Down the Fat Walk to the Lea and Three Mills Island and, again, *they shall not pass!* Nothing can travel further north on this Viking artery, now cleared of its industrial sludge. But a river that can no longer flow freely to the sea is not a river, it's a medieval moat, water enslaved to protect the royal hoopla competition, corralled and cleansed for photo-opportunities and A-list smoked-salmon parties. Across Stratford High Street towards the Olympian shopping village at Westfield, the algae-smothered Lea hits the security buffer of bright yellow barrier buoys monitored by a Metropolitan Police speedboat. Further on upstream, on the other side of the military/sporting/shopping complex, the despoliation continues, and protection through occupation looks set to fail.

Let battle commence.

Surface-to-air missile installations on an apartment block roof in the Bow Quarter. A bizarre military devolution – is this the New Localism? With relief, perhaps, in the COBRA bunker, that Gorgeous George and his allies now reign in confused exile in the north, somewhere along the Bradford/Blackburn corridor? HMS Ocean has arrived and anchored off Deptford Creek. The ship's helicopters batter the dank Thames air, the thumping and thudding echoing off the city towers, while silhouetted cormorants cower on the sewage barges. Twin blades cut smoother through the east London evening.

Lockdown looms for those of us who choose to stay for the party. French Foreign Legionnaires have free reign to shoot in Dover. Dirty-bomb screening has been installed in the car transporter queues by the good burghers of Calais. All for our own protection. On the south-eastern edge of Hackney Marshes, private security companies with names like "Care and Justice" have been contracted to run our internal border controls, patrolling the perimeter of the shopping-centre-cum-games zone in fluorescent uniforms visible from the moon, swabbing steering wheels, dragging reluctant sniffer dogs scared of the local pit bulls. What's in that bag sir? A rogue cauliflower and some potentially deadly Fairy Liquid.

No Pasarán.

above & below
the Lea at Old Ford Lock
left & page 72
City Mill River at Blaker Road
opposite
White Post Lane

HMS Ocean, the largest ship in the Royal Navy, is now moored at the mouth of Deptford Creek. She's too big to pull right up to the pier, so she sits in mid-river, and little boats ferry visitors back and forth. I can't imagine how they're going to sail her up the Lea when the fighting starts, but – what would I know about naval strategy? Despite the hat, I'm not an admiral of the fleet.

And, last Monday, the bank holiday, us local residents were invited on board, to sit in helicopters and play with machine guns and get our faces daubed with camouflage paint just like real soldiers and generally mosey about and nosey around as much as we pleased, even up on the flight deck, around the perimeter of which there's no guard rail, because... well, it's an aircraft carrier, and a guard rail would get in the way of the aircraft. Though they have nets to catch anyone who absent-mindedly walks off the edge.

"What about Health & Safety?" we asked a smiling sailor.

"Oh," he said, "we don't worry about Health & Safety in the Royal Navy."

STUNT CORGI

SANKA COFFIE

A normal day in the LOCOG marketing department. A woman from the ceremonies team dropping into reception. Me going to meet her to pick up the 2012 products they've been using at the palace. For some video or something – they were keeping things hush-hush, as always. Then us making some small talk about how the shoot had gone.

And then her saying this: "Well, the Queen was great, she really played along with the James Bond idea, and actually made some suggestions about how the whole thing should work. We wanted to get stunt dogs in but we had to use her corgis, which was a bit of a challenge, but overall she was great and we think we really got it nailed for the entrance film up to the part where her stunt double jumps into the helicopter with Bond. We're filming the helicopter take-off and flight to the Park later…"

And then her slowing down, trailing off, suddenly looking a little worried. And me nodding and smiling, clamping my jaws to stop the lower one sinking.

And smiling again on a Friday night in July, thinking of the secret I'd kept hidden all this time, waiting for a woman to turn around.

Last week, the Ministry of Defence held a Q&A session in Blackheath Library to address any concerns local residents might have about the Government's unexpected decision to station surface-to-air missiles outside the TA Centre. Despite high levels of security, the proceedings were covertly recorded by undercover librarian Ian Rankin,[1] and we're very grateful to her for sending us the following transcript. We join events just as Brigadier Keith Orville-Harris steps up to the microphone.

MH

BRIG. KEITH ORVILLE-HARRIS: First question, please. Yes, you sir – the man at the back.

MAN AT THE BACK: Where would an aircraft fall if it was hit by a missile fired from Blackheath?

BRIG. KEITH ORVILLE-HARRIS: That would depend on the direction, speed and height of the aircraft. At this particular point in time, I'm afraid it's not possible to give a precise answer.

MAN AT THE BACK: At what point in time *will* it be possible to give a precise answer?

BRIG. KEITH ORVILLE-HARRIS: Generally speaking, we prefer not to say until the height of the aircraft is approaching zero. Anything prior to that would be pure speculation, and there's no place for speculation in the modern army. Yes, the lady in the red coat.

LADY IN THE RED COAT: Would the Government compensate for any damage caused in the event of a hostile aircraft being shot down?

BRIG. KEITH ORVILLE-HARRIS: Everything will be assessed on a case-by-case basis, madam. In the meantime, we suggest you identify the most vulnerable parts of your house, and photograph them to support any later claim for damage. Similarly with the most vulnerable members of your family. And ensure that all clothing has name tags. Yes, the man waving the letter?

MAN WAVING THE LETTER: This came last week, from Greenwich Council. It says the Government is putting arrangements in place to ensure the safety and security of the Olympic Games…

BRIG. KEITH ORVILLE-HARRIS: That's absolutely correct. Thank you for your support. Next?

MAN WAVING THE LETTER: … I hadn't finished. My point is, shouldn't the Government's role actually be to ensure the safety and security of me and my family, not that of a… of a two-week jamboree of running, jumping and, and… splashing?

BRIG. KEITH ORVILLE-HARRIS: Sir, with all due respect, I think you're being somewhat emotional. There's no place for emotion in the modern army.

MAN WAVING THE LETTER: Emotional? So, if there's an attack, we're supposed to… do what? Just lie down and offer a short prayer to St Alfege?[2] Let ourselves be sacrificed so that the Basketball Arena might live on in perpetuity?

BRIG. KEITH ORVILLE-HARRIS: Sir, that is clearly absurd. LOCOG have made it perfectly clear on several occasions that the Basketball Arena is a temporary structure. Now, let's move on, please. Yes, the lady holding the *Daily Mail*.

MAN WAVING THE LETTER: *[shouting]* At what point did everyone go mad? Was it before or after they built the cable car?[4]

BRIG. KEITH ORVILLE-HARRIS: *[loudly]* Madam, your question, please.

LADY HOLDING THE DAILY MAIL: Thank you. *[Reads from piece of paper.]* Will the deployment of Ground-Based Air Defence near my residence invalidate my home insurance policy?

BRIG. KEITH ORVILLE-HARRIS: Ah – I'm afraid you'll really need to take that one up with your insurer, madam.

LADY HOLDING THE DAILY MAIL: It's just that you seem to be saying there's a slight chance that a hijacked 747 might be shot down over our house and we were wondering whether we were covered by our current policy, or whether we needed to get the roof strengthened – I mean the kitchen roof, not the main one.

It's flat, you see, a flat roof, and the homebuyer's report said it wasn't strong enough to be used as a terrace, even though we can get out through the landing window and we've had Ann and Robert over twice now for drinks and it's been fine. Well, Ann nearly fell off last weekend showing us how to do the Macarena, but that's hardly your fault. I know some people are very quick to criticise the army, but I'm not one of them. The boy over the road has just got back from Helmand, and he's ever so nice. Always says hello, asks us how we are. No, she'd just been overdoing the G&Ts. Ever since Robert's affair with that woman from Iceland, she's... I mean the supermarket, not... which I think is what really hurt, actually... she wasn't particularly exotic... he'd only popped in to buy a frozen lasagne... basically, we're covered for Earth, Wind and Fire,[5] but I'm not sure about aeroplanes. That's my question.

BRIG. KEITH ORVILLE-HARRIS: Again, madam, this really *is* one for your insurer – there's no place for Earth, Wind and Fire in the modern army. Yes, the man in the peaked cap with the suitcase-on-wheels?

MAN IN THE PEAKED CAP WITH THE SUITCASE-ON-WHEELS: Is it still safe to fly from City Airport?

BRIG. KEITH ORVILLE-HARRIS: Sorry, what – there's an airport?

[Transcript ends.]

1. Not her actual name, but she's requested anonymity.
2. 11th-century bishop who was boned to death in Greenwich by Vikings.[3]
3. Not as much fun as it sounds. He was pelted with ox bones.
4. Note to readers of the 10th edition. In 2012, a cable car was constructed to connect one of the service roads behind the Excel Centre to somewhere not too long a walk from the O2. No one was entirely sure why. At low tide, you may still be able to see the remains of one of the pylons.
5. Disco/funk band from Chicago notorious for randomly attacking people's houses with sledgehammers and industrial power tools.

This piece was inspired by the Frequently Asked Questions section of the (absolutely genuine) MOD leaflet *Further Information on Armed Forces Supporting Olympic Security on Blackheath Common*. The Man In The Peaked Cap's question was made up; the rest are real, as is the gist of most of the replies.

Oh, and the guns, they're real too.

Being and Nothingness is a Warm Baguette

Matt Haynes

As denizens of Greenwich nervously await the arrival of the dancing horses, the full ramifications of Café Rouge's recent decision to bring a little slice of Continental café culture to the Royal Borough – not, as you might expect, in a raffia basket with a small pot of jam, but in the form of a pavement seating area at the bottom of Stockwell Street – are, I think, being overlooked.

Now, obviously the management have their eye on the impending influx of dressage aficionados, many of whom are, I hear, unable to appreciate the finer points of piaffe, passage or pirouette without an overpriced pain au chocolat inside them. But I think their efforts could unwittingly deliver one of the Games' more unlikely legacies: the reinvention of Greenwich, Deptford and New Cross – London's Lower East Side – as a hotbed of philosophising, Rive Gauche-style. Just picture it! – Thames Poly (or "Greenwich University" as we're supposed to call it these days) as a transpontine Sorbonne; Greenwich High Road refashioned as the Boulevard Saint-Germain of SE10; and black-bereted bands of south London Sartres and Cockney Camuses... Camu's... Camus's... hunched over small round tables passionately wrestling not just with the most provocative philosophical conundrums of our age but also, occasionally, maybe after an absinthe or two, with the most provocative south London Simone de Beauvoirs.

And, in these dark days of *TOWIE*, *Downton* and Fearne Cotton, anything that encourages philosophical wrestling must be a good thing, surely? *What should one do when personal freedom is in conflict with public responsibility? What role has the decline of Western liberalism played in the rise of right-wing nationalism? What the fuck is the point of TfL's service updates stating whether or not either cable-car terminal is out of action when a cable car with only one functioning terminal is, for all practical purposes, a kite?* All these are valid topics for debate, yes, but what *really* matters is that, for the first time in years, here on the banks of Deptford Creek, beards are being stroked and pipes are being smoked, literally, metaphorically and – on occasion – simultaneously.

And it matters because this born-again desire to question the nature of being and the essence of nothingness will, I believe, be infectious. As I passed by Café Rouge this morning, for instance, on my way to get the paper from Sabo's, a stiff-aproned waiter was grimly stabbing some half-deflated balloons with a steak knife – a prelude, I assume, to tying plump new ones on the railings in their stead. But, as he pierced each rubbery skin in turn, one balloon broke free, and – caught by the light July breeze – sailed off up the High Road. The waiter paused, his fist still tight around the knife's thick black shank, and an expression of existential foreboding passed across his face; it was as though he was watching not a red balloon but his own hopes and dreams slipping out of reach and disappearing in the general direction of Deptford Bridge.

A week ago, before the pavement seating, I'm sure he'd just have carried on stabbing.

He looked the sort.

Near the boating lakes at Leytonstone, and the Blackwall Tunnel at Bow, we have seen men wearing camouflage. They came with the rain, but now the sun is coming out. A few miles away as the crows fly, missiles gleam on our roofs.

... in other news, LOCOG has denied openly mocking motorists in south-east London with its new Olympic road closures.

THE OLYMPIC CAFE: HOWARD COLYER

Hello, Babe!

What's going on?

Why d'you send me this text?

Just send me his number.

Text me his number!

Is he in Morocco?

What does this text mean?

Don't worry, Babe, I'll sort it out.

He thinks he can do what he wants because he's in another country.

My friend is a major in Casablanca!

The police.

He'll give him a call.

I'm going to fuck him up.

Text me his number.

Text me his number!

CID Casablanca!

Don't worry, Babe, I'll sort it out.

Or so said the man beside me in the cafe in Greenwich recently renamed for the Games.

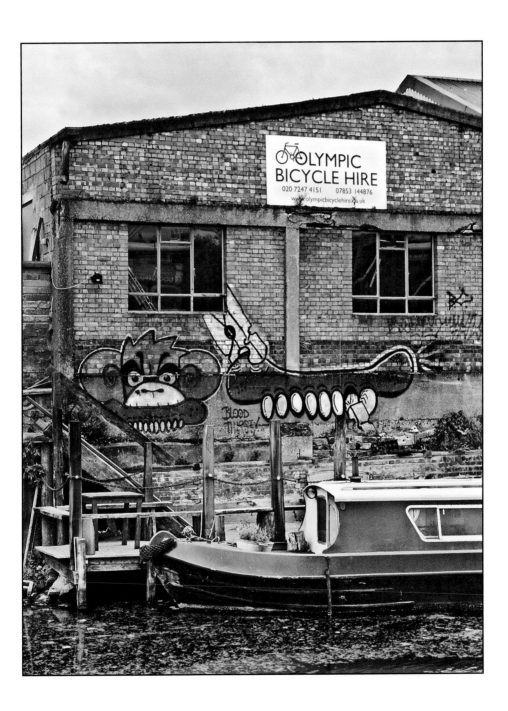

THE SONG OF THE OLYMPIC BINMAN

MATT HAYNES

Last week, Greenwich Council sent us a letter telling us that, during the Games, our bins would be emptied in the middle of the night so that all dustcarts could be well clear of the area by the time spectators started arriving for the equestrian events in the park. They've also supplied us with special Olympic bin bags; if we use these instead of wheelie bins, they say, the vehicles won't have to use their mechanical lifts, and noise can be kept to a minimum. For the binmen, it's unsociable hours, with more physical work, but at least the money's good. For residents, on the other hand, it just feels like yet another imposition, and follows hard on the news that not only will our streets be closed to traffic most days, but Greenwich station will be "exit-only" during morning peaks...

I am a binman for the council
And I walk the back roads,
Searchin' in the dark for another bag to load.

I hear we mustn't use our bin lifts,
I hear you will not like their whine;
And the SE10 binman must be gone by nine.

You can't get into Greenwich station;
Hippophiles are constrained
And, if they know our carts are out,
Won't ever leave their trains.

And you need us more than want us,
And you don't want us at this time;
But the SE10 binman is on good overtime...

PASSENGERS ARE REMINDED THAT THE LAST SET OF DOORS ARE NOT MAGIC

MATT HAYNES

A few months ago, I attended a LOCOG presentation in Devonport House to find out just what us residents of SE10 should expect this Olympic Summer. I came away with the general impression that, from July to September, we should expect to stay indoors with the curtains drawn. And that, if we *absolutely* had to leave the house to buy more tinned goods, we would need to do so in a clockwise direction, having first notified Seb Coe of our intentions via a dedicated phone line; otherwise, Greenwich town centre could witness scenes unwitnessed since the last helicopter left Saigon, the Bolsheviks stormed the Winter Palace, or that Mexican meteorite landed on all the dinosaurs (I still have no idea what all the dinosaurs were doing in Yucatan, but that's the thing about evolution – at the end of the day, or epoch, it all comes down to chance and spur-of-the-moment holiday plans). Also, if we *did* decide to make a run for it, we would need to bear in mind that Cutty Sark station would be mostly closed in case DLR passengers pumped up with Olympic euphoria like a sprinter on stanozolol tried to use the first two sets or last two sets of doors which WOULD NOT OPEN… as the in-carriage announcements repeatedly say…

We're now one week from D-Day, and lockdown has commenced. An eight-lane footbridge has been built over Romney Road. Up on the heath, another straddles the A2. Bus routes have been diverted, and stops disguised with yellow hoods. And, in a ruse borrowed from World War II, when fingerposts in Kent were removed to trick any Nazi invasion force that hadn't thought to bring a map into getting horribly lost on the outskirts of Maidstone, the road sign pointing the way to Greenwich station has had its text obliterated with grey paint. Around the market, meanwhile, large plastic barricades are in place to keep visitors to the prescribed route and so reduce the risk of unpremeditated purchase of a poncho, home-made falafel, or pre-owned biscuit tin. So much, then, for the economic benefits which were supposed to be Greenwich's just reward for having its park hidden behind two-metre-high plastic fences for most of the summer (I'd been reassured at the presentation that these would be totally opaque, which seemed to rather miss the point of my question, as it's not being stared at by the horses that bothers me).

It all seems a bit of an overreaction. Train maps and bus maps are freely available and, since 1936, anyone has been able to buy, from all good bookshops and without an introductory letter from a GP or justice of the peace, an *A-to-Z*. Can we not just let people use their common sense? And, if they genuinely can't find their way out of a DLR carriage with (to be frank) a multiplicity of doors, preferring instead to bump repeatedly against the glass like a trapped bluebottle, or can't manage to walk from a station to a large park six hundred yards away – a large park containing a big hill with an observatory on top – without a man in a pink gilet shouting instructions at them through a loudhailer, then… should they really be allowed in the vicinity of horses? They're temperamental animals.

It's this new one-way system that's the bugger, though. As I understand it, once I leave our front door, I'll have to turn right. And that's going to be really disruptive, because I have a routine. Every morning, I make a pot of tea, then walk to Sabo's to buy the paper; by the time I've returned, the tea is nicely brewed. Result: happiness. But, next week, once I've bought the paper, button-eyed youngsters with giant foam hands are going to chase me up Greenwich High Road towards Deptford Bridge; and, when I finally make it back to the house, the tea will be nicely stewed. Result: misery. I suppose I could pop into Puccino's in the station for a latte, but… it will almost certainly be closed, in case people start trying to use it.

You know what? I've had enough of this.

I'm going to Düsseldorf.

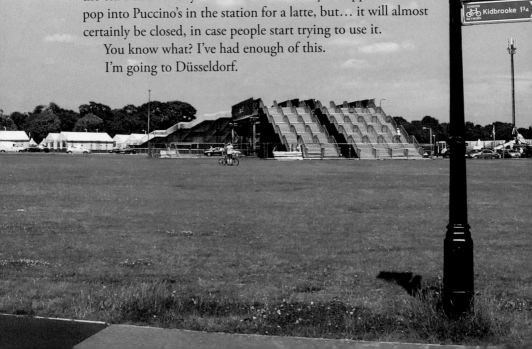

🇬🇧

the building on your
right is magnificent,
but it is not the station.

🇫🇷

le bâtiment à droite,
c'est magnifique, mais
ce n'est pas la gare.

*... meanwhile,
residents of
Leyton are
warned that
Ruckholt Road
is 574 metres
away from
something.*

Bus stop closed

Towards Blackheath,
Charlton or Surrey Quays

| 177 | 180 | 199 |
| 386 | | |

London 2012
ROAD CLOSED

28/7/12 & 29/7/12	7am-11am	&	2pm-7pm
30/7/12	7am-2pm	&	3pm-8pm
31/7/12	7am-noon	&	2pm-7pm
2/8/12 to 3/8/12	8am-noon	&	1pm-6pm
4/8/12			7am-4pm
5/8/12			8am-5pm
6/8/12			8am-8pm
7/8/12	7am-11am	&	3pm-7pm
8/8/12	8am-1pm	&	2pm-7pm
9/8/12			9am-7pm
11/8/12			noon-5pm & 6pm-10pm
12/8/12			11am-4pm & 5pm-9pm

FRESH TO ORDER

Live   Midweek
FLAM   Menu
Dan
&
Gui
the
Su
★ Night... ★

LOCOG:
LICENCE
TO KILL A
TOWN
CENTRE

CHECK POINT ←

STOP if directed

London 2012   london2012.com

CROOMS HILL

ALF: See them bubbles? You know what that is, don'tcha?
EDDIE: Is it...
ALF: Yup, you got it, Eddie boy...
EDDIE: ... Rebecca...
ALF: ... that's one of them terrorist midget submarines, that is...
EDDIE: ... Adlington?
   [pause]
ALF: What?
EDDIE: What?

Across the canal, it begins again, its opening bars echo

echo

echo

the raindrops bouncing on the water. echo

echo

Bah-bah-bah-baaaaaaah.

echo

Bah-bah-bah-baaaaaaah.

echo

Here on Fish Island, we can see the stadium's bulk, but not what's happening inside, beyond that wet, white rim. We can hear the secrets of these final rehearsals, though, those mantras from the deep.

Lager
Lager
Lager

the stadium is telling us.

Shouting

Lager

mega

mega

Lager

white

thing Lager

Jude Rogers (*with thanks to Luke Turner*)

A spokesman for LOCOG today insisted that athletes from
all nations would feel at home in the Olympic Village,
especially those from outlying suburbs of Magnitogorsk.

Waiting for the Apocalypse on the Isle of Dogs

Janet Maitland

Island Gardens, E14. A group of dog walkers ducks as a military helicopter swoops overhead. On the riverside walkway, tourists are taking photos of the huge aircraft carrier moored near the opposite bank. Outside the tea hut, two old men are sitting in the sunshine.

OLD MAN 1: They're aiming straight at us, you know. They've got the doors wide open and they're just standing there pointing their machine guns. One false move and that's it, you're toast. And have you seen that?

OLD MAN 2: What?

OLD MAN 1: That cable up there.

OLD MAN 2: Where?

OLD MAN 1: Up there. Above the trees. I saw it soon as I come down this morning. How the fuck they got it up there I don't know. Look, it goes over the river and then over there somewhere.

OLD MAN 2: What's it for?

OLD MAN 1: God knows, but it'll be something to do with the Olympics. I wouldn't be surprised if they bugged the tea hut while they were at it. You'd better watch what you say. Don't want to get shot for insurrection.

OLD MAN 2: Don't be daft.

OLD MAN 1: Listen, if they can stick nuclear warheads on top of those blocks in Bethnal Green, they can do anything.

They sip their tea. A poodle laps water from the dog bowl by the hut. The sun goes in. Another helicopter flies over, sending crisp packets skipping across the park.

OLD MAN 1: We might as well be in Vietnam. Any minute now and they'll be spraying us with napalm.

They sit in silence.

OLD MAN 2: There's one good thing come out of it, though.

OLD MAN 1: Go on, surprise me.

OLD MAN 2: They opened up the old toilets on Manchester Road this morning. Cleaned them up and everything. Really nice.

OLD MAN 1: But when it's all over they'll close them down again, won't they? No Olympic legacies for us. We'll be back to peeing in the bushes.

The clouds turn the colour of molten sulphur. A line of four helicopters roars over the park.

OLD MAN 2: You going to watch the Opening Ceremony later?

OLD MAN 1: WHAT?

OLD MAN 2: THE OPENING CEREMONY. YOU GOING TO WATCH IT?

OLD MAN 1: OF COURSE I'M NOT GOING TO WATCH IT. SOME MORRIS DANCERS HOPPING ROUND A MAYPOLE? A FEW SHEEP WANDERING ROUND A FIELD? WHAT'S THAT ALL ABOUT, THEN? MILLIONS OF PEOPLE ALL OVER THE WORLD WATCHING, AND ALL WE CAN COME UP WITH IS EMBARRASSING BOLLOCKS. THE SHAME OF IT.

The poodle wanders past, stares at them briefly, then wanders on.

OLD MAN 2: Want more tea?

OLD MAN 1: No, I'm off. It'll be safer indoors.

I WAS AT WORK on the evening of the Opening Ceremony. The building is only eight storeys tall but, through an accident of topography – and because it isn't yet surrounded by other, taller buildings – you can see an impressive slice of London if you pick the right room on the top floor.

When I went up there just after eight o'clock, I thought there would be other people doing the same thing. But I had the place to myself.

I don't think I've been interested in aerobatic displays since I was about twelve – it was an excuse to get away from my desk as much as anything else. So when the planes appeared from the east, trailing red, white and blue, I surprised myself.

I was excited.

They arced over the stadium, where 80,000 people must have watched them for all of five seconds. But, alone on the eighth floor, I watched them carry on, out across the City and the West End, black silhouettes against the sunset; and I watched as they turned to loop back north-east.

And I carried on watching until they disappeared from sight, somewhere in the darkening skies over Essex.

JUST AFTER EIGHT HARRY CAUL

At 2½ square kilometres, the Olympic Park is as big as 357 football pitches.

DANGER DO NOT ENTER

10,490 athletes from more than 200 nations will be competing in the London 2012 Olympic Games compared with 4,104 athletes in 1948.

HORROR!!!

Nine Scenes from a Ceremony

as told to Jude Rogers by Scott Cawley

1 I am sitting under a tree, praying it doesn't rain. If it rains, the water will come through the webbing, which is hung above our heads, and trickle down the staircase supporting the Tor. My flat cap and waistcoat couldn't take it; neither could the bud in my ear. My face is dirty already, so that doesn't matter.

2 I am hearing the drums, and then the crackle on FM Channel 3. Steve's voice. "Remember all those wet days in Dagenham? This is what it was for. Remember – friends for life." Six months ago, we didn't know each other. We had nothing in common. And now here we all are, watching our tree rise into the air.

3 I am weaving down the Tor, across the floor, marching, moving, lifting with my hands, taking away the heavy grass. Sixteen minutes. Somewhere nearby are Windrush passengers, Chelsea Pensioners, suffragettes, steeplejacks; and looms, water wheels, beam engines, chimney stacks. But they are not with me, in this moment. I am here, but not here.

4 I am watching the rings travelling above my head – gentle halos of gold, dripping sheets of light. They join together, but the feeling doesn't overpower us, not yet.

5 I am sweeping the ground as a film plays above me. There is a huge, shocked cheer, although I'm not sure why. I quickly push my broom one last time, then run away, down a corridor, the sound of the blades getting closer. As I do, two men jump out of the helicopter; one of them, I hear later, was wearing a dress.

6 I am walking to the Eton Manor gate, as we've been told to, my heart in my mouth.

7 I am taking a photo of an athlete who's wearing a pink and yellow tunic and a red and green hat with a single star in the middle. He takes a photo of me. Somewhere in Burkina Faso, a sprinter who went out in the first round of the 100 metres now has on his wall a picture of a man from Whitley Bay with a muddy face, dressed up as a Jarrow marcher.

8 I am kneeling on a tube train at Leyton, adjusting my 1930s boots. Next to me sits a man wearing headphones, pretending to not notice. The nurses sit opposite him, laughing, adjusting their old-fashioned hats. Two Asian men smile and nod. The train stops at Stratford. We get out. We can't do anything else.

9 I am sitting in a soulless pub in the Westfield Centre, having my first pint in twelve years. An hour later, I watch the fireworks shoot rainbows into the sky. When the emptiness comes, you will have to fill it with some other part of your life, Danny said. Danny was right. But, right now, this is everything.

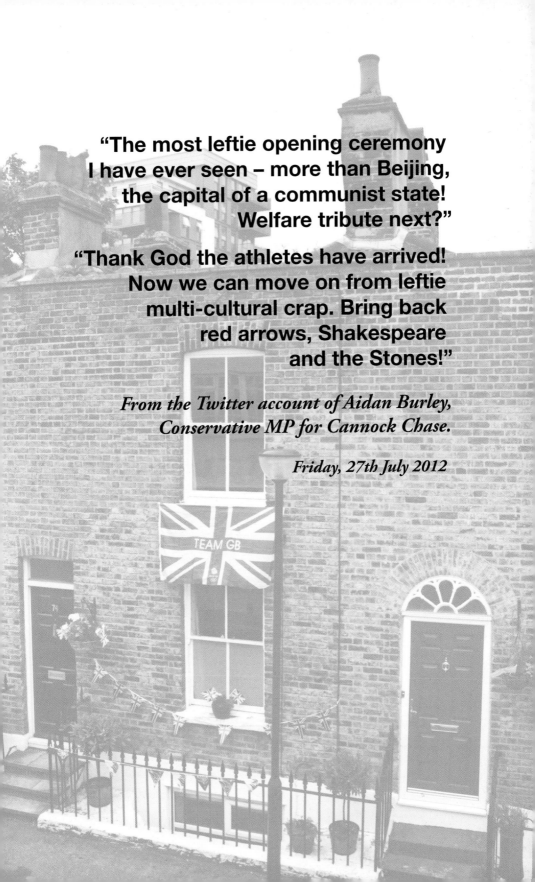

"The most leftie opening ceremony
I have ever seen – more than Beijing,
the capital of a communist state!
Welfare tribute next?"

"Thank God the athletes have arrived!
Now we can move on from leftie
multi-cultural crap. Bring back
red arrows, Shakespeare
and the Stones!"

*From the Twitter account of Aidan Burley,
Conservative MP for Cannock Chase.*

Friday, 27th July 2012

From: Sarah McCartney <sarahmc@myrealaddress.co.uk>
Subject: Fwd: That Olympic Opening Ceremony!
Date: Saturday, 28 July 2012 16:02 BST
To: smoke@smokelondon.co.uk

Begin forwarded message:

From: American Ex-Co-Worker <americanexcoworker@geemail.com>
Date: Saturday, 28 July 2012 09:00 (16:00 BST)
To: British Former Colleague <britishformercolleague@woolies.co.uk>
Subject: That Olympic Opening Ceremony!

Hey, BFC! Remember me? How's it going, hon'? I know it's been, like, years, but I just had to email you about that little ceremony of yours.

It's spun me out so much I thought only a real live British person could explain all that craziness for me. And I don't mean to be, y'know, rude, but I thought the whole thing was weird. You know, your country does pageantry soooo well – those cute guys in the hats with the horses! – so why did that Danny guy choose to show the public health service and a bunch of kids in hospital beds? I don't get how that's uplifting or relevant to England, which we all know can be really cool. And most people give the English public health service really bad marks – right?

Also, the industrial revolution was a horrible time for most Brits, I guess. Horrific factory conditions, child slave labor. Sure, I totally get that one of the points of the ceremony is to showcase all sides of the country, but it should be relevant to the rest of the world too – right? For half of the show none of us got what was going on, when it should've been sweet.

And yeah, of course Mary Poppins was totally the coolest nanny ever, but having her there is totally irrelevant to anyone who isn't Anglo-Saxon, and wasn't born in the 1960s-1970s, like us. Folks from almost anywhere but the US and the UK must have been seriously scratching their heads. And I feel for those guys!

All of that said, it was also pretty endearing, I guess, because the whole muddled thing still managed to be very English – if you know what I mean. They meant really well.

Would be psyched to know what you thought. Hopefully see you sometime – give us a call if you're ever in Utah, man!

Your AXCW x

[… in fifteen minutes, Mo Farah can run five thousand,
eight hundred and twenty-three metres…]

From: Sarah McCartney <britishformercolleague@woolies.co.uk>
Subject: Re: That Olympic Opening Ceremony!
Date: Saturday, 28 July 2012 16:17 BST
To: American Ex-Co-Worker (americanexcoworker@geemail.com)
Bcc: smoke@smokelondon.co.uk

So, AXCW.

Well. I think I have a few words of explanation for you.

I think what you missed was this: that all of us Brits (not English: Brits = English, Scottish, Welsh and Northern Irish, as the ceremony made clear) were glued to the screen, one moment killing ourselves laughing, then killing ourselves crying. We loved that our national heroes were joining together in embracing the completely barmy mixture of reality and fantasy, all of which is part of our culture. It's what made us who we are now.

It's not the "English public health service", incidentally – it's the National Health Service and most people do not give it bad marks. Most of us are very grateful that it's there at all. We don't have to worry about what will happen if and when we get ill, or run over, or when bad luck comes and bites us on the arse (sorry, ass). And, yes, the NHS is pushed sometimes, but at least it's there and if you're ill you can get treated – for nothing. Everyone can.

And the Industrial Revolution was a horrible time, was it? – I'm sorry about that. But neither Britain nor the rest of the world would look the way it does now without it. Yes there were horrific factory conditions, some appalling pollution and abused human beings. But what are we supposed to do – pretend it didn't happen? The steel industry made Tower Bridge. It didn't get there by magic. The Golden Gate Bridge too, for that matter.

This is my favourite line of all of yours, by the way: "They meant really well."

I'm quite a nice person but that's bringing out the worst in me.

I'll pretend it's not there.

Perhaps the rest of Europe, and Japan probably, understood it better than many Americans. We love to take the mickey out of ourselves, and wallow in a bit of self-deprecating humour. And it was supposed to be funny – I think that's probably the biggest cultural gap.

Other countries want to impress the rest of the world with their strength and might (I was shit-scared by China's). We just wanted a bloody good night in by the television.

Does that help? By the way, Danny Boyle, who directed it (and Slumdog Millionaire and Trainspotting) was allowed to do whatever he liked with the Opening Ceremony. There were no managers and no politicians telling him what to do. No approval committee and lots and lots of volunteers. So this was our story, plain and simple.

OK I'm finished.

No I'm not.

Pageantry is for tourists. Yes, we can put on a good show in that sense, especially if it's been going on the same way every day since 1463 or something. But this was for something very different – and it was something new. We all loved the fact that the real Queen took part. When she turned around in the palace, the whole country shouted "Oh My God!" at once. And then everything got summed up by Dizzee Rascal singing Bonkers. We're all walking round today really really proud to be bonkers.

I wonder what people overseas expected. Marching bands and golden coaches? We got reality. We got life as it has been and as it is. We apparently managed to get the first lesbian kiss ever on to Saudi TV. We're proud of that. We have Tim Berners-Lee who gave the world wide web to the world for nothing, and didn't try to patent it because it's more important than money. We also have Isambard Kingdom Brunel who invented the iron-hulled ship and didn't patent it – for the same reason.

Win win.

I'm definitely finished now.

Not in Utah for the foreseeable.

Byeee!

BFC xxxx

On 28 July 2012, at 09:00, American Ex-Co-Worker wrote:

> Hey, BFC! Remember me? How's it going, hon'? I know it's been, like, years, but I just had to email you about that little ceremony of yours.
>
> It's spun me out so much I thought only a real live British person could explain all that craziness for me. And I don't mean to be, y'know, rude, but I thought the whole thing was weird. You know, your country does pageantry soooo well – those cute guys in the hats with the horses! – so why did that Danny guy choose to show the public health service and a bunch of kids in hospital beds? I don't get how that's uplifting or relevant to England, which we all know can be really cool. And most people give the English public health service really bad marks – right?
>
> Also, the industrial revolution was a horrible time for most Brits, I guess. Horrific factory conditions, child slave labor. Sure, I totally get that one of the points of the ceremony is to showcase all sides of the country, but it should be relevant to the rest of the world too – right? For half of the show none of us got what was going on, when it

AFTER THE ROAR

JUDE ROGERS

AFTER THE ROAR, we've been told to expect chaos. When, as always, we emerge from the darkness and that low, heavy rumble, into the bright station, there'll be bodies and noise.

It is 7 p.m. – prime time. The train speeds forward as always. And then it comes to a stop. The doors open on both sides. First the left, then the right. But nothing. Nobody.

The new blue and red cushions gleam under the carriage lights. If you look closely at the fabric, you can see the London Eye. Then the dome of St Paul's and its base, then two tall towers. I see thirty-six of each of these, unhidden, unexpected.

My Central Line train closes its doors and pulls off towards the sanctuary of Mile End. In the window, against the blackness, I see nothing but me.

Somewhere above ground, men are meant to be playing basketball, and women playing hockey. Children might be asking Mum for a Mandeville, and Dad buying plastic bottles splashed with brands. I am travelling from home into the city, a journey I nearly didn't make, a journey I have been warned against making.

But Stratford came and went, silently. And, as I continue west, I wonder where all the people have gone, and why I'm happy that they have.

OLYMPIC TORCH TRILOGY

JACQUELINE DOWNS

Part One

First came the news. It would be London 2012. There was noise – joyful, hopeful noise. Then came the explosions. And noise of a different kind. Desperate, choked, dislocated.

In the seven years that followed there was more noise for Anna – the noise of a heart being smashed in like a door – and also silence, the silence of loss and grief. This would all take some getting over.

Part Two

"Are you fucking kidding me?" Anna, with her gift for misery, had written the dates on the office calendar with a federal-blue Sharpie and a heavy heart, months before the event itself. Beyond the office walls, people spoke of excitement, anticipation, *showing* the rest of the world. Within them, the only comments were about how inconvenient the whole thing was going to be. "I think we can safely say we'll only make it in for work by lunchtime," Anna said, as she scoured the mayor's travel advice. "Seriously, are you fucking kidding me? It tells me to take a different route. Be helpful. Don't clog up the tube network. Yeah, OK, so I could just go to Victoria and then walk. *That* would be a different route. *That* would be helpful, keep me off the tube. BUT THE FUCKING MALL IS CLOSED AND YOU CAN'T GO THROUGH ST JAMES'S PARK. Because of some VOLLEYBALL. Is that even an Olympic sport? Is it?"

"You could try walking around the *whole* of Green Park, then down…" Kate began.

"I can't even look at you right now," Anna replied. "Or this fucking travel leaflet."

―――――――――――――――――――――――――

Though exhausted by loss and by her attempts to be joyful, hopeful, Anna began looking, actively looking, for someone to take the loneliness away. Not possible, of course. That was an inside job; she knew that. But she started smiling at people at parties, her teeth bared like piano keys, in a way that she hoped was winning, but was probably just awkward, maybe even a little frightening. Then, like something out of a story, she found John, five weeks before Operation Incon-fucking-venience, as it had become known in the office.

On their first date he suggested a walk along the river; he thought it would be romantic, a Richard Curtis film. The rain sliced through the air like blunted nail scissors and made her hair go puffy, like Crystal Tipps', a reference he didn't get; one of many reminders of the ten years of distance between them.

It was over sips of icy whiskey in plastic cups at the bar in the Royal Festival Hall that he revealed it to her. "I'm in the Opening Ceremony," he said. "But I can't tell you what I'm doing in it, because it's top secret." She found his pride, his gift for cheeriness, almost touching. Her eyes said, "I couldn't care less." Her mouth said, "Oh, right. Nice. Fun. Yep, sure, feel free to keep all of that to yourself."

She was surprised when he wanted to see her again; she was more surprised that she kind of wanted to see him.

As Operation Incon-fucking-venience moved closer, John moved away a little. All those rehearsals. All that secrecy. All that – happiness. But he called when he could and, although she tried not to, she laughed during those calls, as they talked about everything except That Which Could Not Be Discussed.

He takes this pretty seriously, she thought. Fuckwit.

"I'll be pretty busy for the next two weeks," he told her. "Rehearsals every day." She felt some relief; maybe a little sadness. But not so much. Still fighting the pain of loss, still not wanting to invite more of it in through that heart like a smashed-in door.

At some point during those two weeks the torch started its journey across the country. Apparently. She wasn't paying that much attention. She demonstrated a flicker of interest when it arrived in Southend, where she had misspent her youth. She watched the news, wondering if she'd recognise anyone from the screaming, delighted crowds. She knew she wouldn't; it was another life. Everyone she'd known back then was gone. She looked at these people, their uncontained joy, their complete immersion in this mayhem, and she couldn't recognise them at all.

So, she was shocked to find herself wondering if she should take the day off work when the torch came through her neighbourhood; found herself wishing she'd been in Lewisham to see Doreen Lawrence grasping it in her dignified hands. That's what they said about her: dignified. Insulting, really. Yet another loss so explosive that dignity shouldn't be mentioned in the same sentence. Let her cry and rail and scream at us all, was Anna's view. Let her always remind us of what was taken from her. No one should have to keep that kind of thing quiet.

She tried hard to start smiling again, and went for dinner with another man on the night of the Opening Ceremony. They entered the pub as Croatia was entering the stadium. "Is this all there is to it?" she thought. Then she stopped thinking.

Listening to Alice and Tom the next day she had that familiar cold, hollow feeling of being left out, left behind. They spoke in wonder of painted faces, metal rings, alien patriotism. Catch-up TV gave her the gift of joining in, coming to the party late as usual. She sat slack-jawed as men in stovepipe hats danced, nurses twirled around hospital beds, stage-school children beamed through fake sickness, dozens of Mary Poppins floated, David Beckham looked embarrassed in a speedboat. Crowds screeched, their open mouths like baby birds hungry for worms. They're already thinking about how they will remember this for the rest of their lives, Anna thought; how it's the biggest and the best thing that's ever happened to them. Fuckwits.

When the torch was put to rest she felt something like salt in her eyes, so she texted John, hopefully and fearfully. "Mary Poppins? Dancing nurse? Welder?" she asked. His reply took some time to come, but when it did she knew she would struggle to look kindly at him again. "Stovepipe hat," he said. She replied straight away: "I don't think this is working."

Part Three

She was with Alice and Tom again, walking along Westow Hill, listening to them talking of cycling and swimming and hockey, when she saw the sign in the window of the cupcake café. "Oh, there's an Olympic torch over th…" she began. Alice was across the road before the sentence was fully out of Anna's mouth. She and Tom had no option but to follow. It was true. There it was. An empty mesh construct of scrambled gold. There was a photographer. A union flag. Anna thought how, aside from the cupcakes, she had stumbled across three of the things she hated most in the world. "You guys go ahead," she sighed. "I'll do what I always do." She watched as Alice and then Tom posed in front of the flag, joining in. Being part of it.

And then, of course, it happened. Before she knew what she was doing, Anna had stopped them wrapping up the flag and packing away the torch. She'd cried out, "I'll do it!" and had stood smiling and gracious, gazing at the torch as though it had given her back her life. Part of the team. One of them. "You look happy," said Alice.

———————————————

Anna texted John. "See her eyes, they are bright tonight." She presumed, maybe hoped, it would be another reference that he wouldn't get. His reply was instant. "See how they light your way tonight."

GIRL: So, which way do we go?

BOY: [lugging case behind] Look! There's signs further up.

GIRL: Oh, yes, the big pink si... [hops, skips and jumps up to them] Oh.

BOY: [shouting over] What's the matter?

GIRL: I don't understand. How do we...?

BOY: How do we, what? Just see which way they are pointi... [catches up] Oh.

[they pause]

GIRL: Maybe it's like *Harry Potter*. You know, that bit where he goes to where he's supposed to go and find platform 9¾, and it's not there, but when he stands up really close to it, it suddenly is.

BOY: Or that bit at the beginning of *Labyrinth* where Sarah thinks she's looking at this endless brick wall, but there's actually a way through.

GIRL: Then she finds David Bowie in those tight leggings.

[they pause]

BOY: Are you OK?

GIRL: Erm, yes, just thinking about David Bowie in those leggings.

[they pause]

GIRL: They'd be pretty good for the rhythmic gymnastics.

Two Olympic Haikus

Matt Haynes

[ONE]

On The Road Back To Greenwich Station

He smiles to greet them;
The shoulder-mounted toddler
High-fives his giant hand.

[TWO]

In The Grounds Of The Old Royal Naval College

They smile for photos;
Their shoulder-mounted rifles
Brush the toddler's hair.

GREENWICH
MARKET
SUPPORT LOCAL
SHOPS
←

LINDY LOOKED OUT of the sitting-room window, and saw horses. They were running through the boating lake and jumping in front of the children's playground.

Then she looked at the TV in the corner of the room. They were running through the lake there, too. They were jumping in front of the playground as well. They were smaller there, though, so little you could squeeze them between your fingers. But Lindy knew they were real, because she could hear their clip-clops in two places: on the channel with the sport on, and in the park opposite her granny's.

30th July was Lindy's fourth birthday. Her mum wasn't sure how much effort she had to put into their celebration – Lindy didn't always know what was going on, after all. Mum decided a party in Greenwich Park would be the answer, but she picked the only day that Greenwich Park was completely closed because of the showjumping. So now here they were, deliciously trapped in her mother's house, three generations of Lloyd girls, looking uphill.

The horses ran, and so did they. From the glass of the window to the glass of the cathode ray. At first, it felt miraculous, but Lindy quickly understood how it worked: that the horses could be both there and here. She sat down in front of the TV, and ate her birthday cake happily. After all, it was even more exciting to be allowed to eat it in Granny's sitting room.

It may not be a birthday Lindy remembers, but it will be one her mother and grandmother will. Sitting in a house they have known for most of their lives, their eyes dashing left and right, feeling magic happen.

HORSES

JUDE

ROGERS

with

KATHERINE

LLOYD

Benson, the Talking Horse
16 St Alfege Passage, Greenwich

Gaaaaabon, Gaaaaabon, Gaaabon, Gaaabon, Gabon! Gabon! GABON!!!

LUKE UPTON

South Korea vs Gabon. When I'd applied, I'd obviously hoped for a Team GB game or perhaps Brazil or Mexico, but – no, the pride of francophone West Africa were set to take on what one Australian newspaper called "Good Korea", and I had four tickets. My girlfriend immediately said she didn't want to go. But I had three friends who'd watched enough terrible football matches in their time to want in.

We immediately sensed we'd be backing Gabon. Their gold and blue kit, complete anonymity on the global football scene, and possession of a midfielder called André Biyogo Poko made "Les Panthères" the team for us. Wikipedia and Google built up our knowledge of the little African republic, and we soon learnt that Gabon had never met South Korea in a football match; this was going to be huge.

To be true fans, we needed flags; we would be proud to wrap ourselves in the green (representing the forests), gold (the equator) and blue (the sea) of their tricolour. A couple were swiftly purchased online. Next, T-shirts; five were bought in the same green, gold and blue, and we wrote a letter on each: G-A-B-O-N. On the back, in a nod to the team's nickname, we wrote G-R-R-R-R.

With our flags draped around our shoulders, we arrived for a pre-match lunchtime pint at The Globe by Baker Street station looking like British-born West African superheroes. Disappointingly, Gabon's favourite brew, Régab, wasn't on tap. Surely a huge missed opportunity? An American couple were intrigued by our GABO garb. "What's a Gabon?" asked the wife when we showed her the spare N in its carrier bag. They were from South Carolina and had come over for the Games, but failed to get tickets. They were, however, pleased to have seen Boris Johnson on the tube, and said they'd drunk "bucketfuls" every day. Being good Americans, they wanted a snap. And so it was that the husband became the first person to don the N; wearing what I always think of as classic CIA-agent gear – chinos, polo shirt (now hidden) and wraparound Oakley sunglasses – he proudly stood in the G-A-B-O-N line and pledged his lifelong support to Les Panthères.

Part of me just knows this picture of us is now up on a mantelpiece in Greenville, SC, right beside the wedding photo.

Walking towards the stadium, we were shocked at the crowds – the lure of Gabon truly was strong. We were also surprised, and perhaps even a little disappointed, to see other Londoners in Gabon flags and shirts; an investigation into the Gabon-flag-sales algorithm was probably already under way at Amazon UK. As we climbed the stand, the tension was becoming unbearable: who would be sitting at the end of our row of four seats, and so get the chance to wear the N?

It was a mother with two small boys. She confirmed that she would be supporting the 'bon, but made it equally clear she wouldn't be wearing our T-shirt. Instead, she volunteered her husband, who was just returning with crisps and pop. Looking confused and a bit reluctant, he took a deep breath, sucked in his stomach, and put it on.

So there we were, a splash of green, gold and blue on the top tier, cheering our boys as they ran out onto the pitch. Then came the anthem. We had prepared ourselves for this, having found the words online, and belted out *La Concorde* in our best French accents:

Et chasse les sorciers, ces perfides trompeurs
Qui semaient le poison et répandaient la peur.

(And banish the sorcerers, those perfidious deceivers
Who sowed poison and spread fear.)

There were other songs later.

Gaaaaabon, Gaaaaabon,
Gaaabon, Gaaabon,
Gabon! Gabon!
GABON!

(To the tune of *I'm the Leader of the Gang* by Gary Glitter.)

G.A.B.O.N., G.A.B.O.N.

(To the tune of *D.I.S.C.O.* by Ottawan.)

Woooohoooo, we're halfway there. Wooohoooo Gabon on a prayer.

(To the tune of *Living on a Prayer* by Bon Jovi.)

After the ninety minutes we were hoarse, tired, but proud. Our boys had held the vastly superior South Korea to a goalless draw. Walking away from the ground, we knew we didn't want this wonderful day to end, but London has no "Little Gabon", and Google searches for Gabon bars or restaurants failed to deliver. We considered heading to the Gabon embassy, but it shuts on Wednesday afternoons. So we went to the pub, and watched Team GB on the television, and cheered nowhere near as much as we had for Gabon. But then our thoughts were already on how to get to Rio, for the next chapter in the Gabon story; we do, after all, already have the flags, the T-shirts, and the songs.

Ten to – ow! – eight – ow! – at Paddington – OW!

"It's like this every morning," a girl mumbles,
her mouth muffled by the raincoated armpit
of a stranger.

"Not on a bloody Saturday," her friend mutters.
"If only that site worked, I wouldn't have had to get
these fucking tickets," she adds, then offers a forlorn
"Jesus Shitting Christ."

Rescue comes in the form of a foam hand.
It waggles gently from a gap in the big squash of
bodies. "Eton Dorney!" squeals its owner,
her other hand, much smaller, wrapped tightly
around the leg of her mother. The carriage erupts.

Our train leaves the platform, and we row, row,
row our boat.

both bystanding observations by **Jude Rogers**

At Hampton Court Palace, he sits on his throne.
His hair curls onto his forehead; it touches
his cheekbones. He raises his hands towards
his subjects, and they cheer for him, just as
Cardinal Wolsey would have wanted,
five hundred years ago, on this same spot.

Those long, regal fingers become victory
signs, and the regal attire – sweaty polyester
– gets unzipped to a pigeony belly. The crowd
salutes their king, in the only way they can:
"Wiiiii-GOOOOOOOO."

THE EASTWAY CYCLE CIRCUIT used to be near here. We rode one hundred laps around it in 2006, celebrating what we used to have in the weeks before it went.

Six years later, just before the Games, the part of Eastway by the Olympic Park was closed to cyclists. So was the right turn from Eastway to Homerton Road. If you called Get Ahead Of The Games to check what to do instead, you'd get no reply. If you just turned up at the junction, confused, as I did, officials would simply wave you through.

For five days, I made 180-degree turns through heavy traffic; being told I was right, knowing I was doing something wrong. On the evening of Wednesday, 1st August, cyclist Dan Harris was killed by an Olympic bus while trying to exit Eastway into Ruckholt Road.

By the Community Woodland, underneath the A12 flyover, another Olympic legacy lives on.

EASTWAY

Ian Hunter

with Jude Rogers

THE SOUND OF LEYTON

JUDE ROGERS

Through our white-painted back door, I can hear a sound swirling around the yard.

"Urrrrrrrggggh," it goes. "Urrrrrrrrgh."

I don't know what it is.

I carry on working. Tap-tap-tap on my laptop. It's August, and it's hot. The heat beats its way in from outside, takes over the house.

"Waaaaarrgggggghhh!"

This sound is better. Happier, almost. It sounds a little like voices coming together, but it's the traffic on the A12, certainly. It's always a low hum here in Leyton, growling gently a few streets away. And there's got to be more of it at the moment, what with the Olympics happening down the road; there have to be more lorries and vans and people who are ridi…

One minute.

BBC iPlayer on.

"Waaaaaaaargh!"

We are live. There is a girl on the screen. Her name is Victoria. She is a 32-year-old cyclist from Bedfordshire. She has just won a race, and has tears in her eyes. Later, she will get a medal, gold and heavy, hung around her neck.

I turn the sound off, and click on Google Maps.

Through the back door, I hear the rumble that has travelled up from Park Live, past the Copper Box, out of Eton Manor Gate, and along Ruckholt Road. That has turned left into York Road, then danced across Coronation Gardens, past the maze where the children play, the bandstand, the memorial. That has turned left at the new Kebabish, passed Orient Furniture House, Flying Carpets (London) Ltd, and then swung to the right. That has rolled, surged, waaaaaaarghed along the grey, sweaty tarmac, bounced off the parked cars, ricocheted off the terraced houses. The rumble that has landed, and now circles, like a whirlpool, in my yard.

On the small screen, Victoria's smile casts a beam of light. The smile travels the mile from her to here faster than her wheels, but not, it seems, than that sound.

Scene: a pop-up pub on Leyton High Road. It is 5th August, 2012.
Two men in their twenties sit at a small table, on two mismatched chairs,
holding pints of real ale.

SAM: Bloody hell, look at her by the bar, Dave. She's six fucking feet.

DAVE: Sam!

SAM: What?

DAVE: *[whispering]* Keep your voice down, you knob-head.

SAM: *[also whispering]* How does a woman get that tall, Dave?

DAVE: Er, her parents are tall, maybe she's ate her veg…

SAM: *[shouting again]* Dave, there's bloody two of them!

> *To their left, a woman with a high ponytail has just left the toilet door*
> *swinging behind her. The men watch her walk back to her seat.*
> *She's only five metres away from them now.*

SAM: Are they foreign, Dave?

DAVE: They look foreign. They definitely don't look Leyton.

> *The two women turn their bodies around, catch the eyes of the men,*
> *and raise their pints of bitter high in the air.*

SAM: Well, would you look at that – Czech flag, innit?

DAVE: Yes it is, Sam.

> *[silence]*

SAM: You all right, Dave?

> *Dave stares at the women as they turn back to the bar.*

DAVE: Those girls would throw you into a net and drink your beer,
Sam. I think I'm in love.

Sankt Andreas Hotel
Düsseldorf

See those horses up
there? On the TV? In the
corner beside the bar?
Well, I live just... no,
sorry, I don't know much
about handball, is it...
fun?

OF COURSE IT'S BECAUSE I'M A LONDONER

CHRIS LONG

Look, I'm not trying to be difficult, but I'm a third-generation south Londoner, I wasn't born to "join in"; I was brought up to keep myself to myself and stay out of trouble. I can be as enthusiastic as the next bloke but, you know: within bounds.

We went to the Olympics, my Significant Other, Other Half – Helen, I think she prefers to be called – and me. Obviously I didn't want to go – all that hype on the telly and the idea of wading through even more tourists than usual was a real turn-off. And then there was fucking Boris coming out of loudspeakers all over the place, telling us "there's going to be huge pressure on the transport network". Really? No shit, Sherlock.

The TFL website suggested we get off at West Ham and then WALK to Stratford. I'm a Londoner; I don't need a website to tell me how to get to east London, I need a tube map. A train to Waterloo and then the Jubilee Line to Stratford worked just fine. So much for changing at Canada Water, or Mile End, or… West 23rd Street.

Wankers.

Stratford was swarming with people. Happy, smug "we've got tickets to the Olympics" people. Yeah, well, I had tickets too, and I managed not to show off by grinning at everyone. Closer to the stadium, the Games Makers, in vile off-pink uniforms fitting one in ten, started to multiply. "Have your tickets ready," they chanted. Well, yes, that's a good idea.

"Jesus H. Christ," I thought, spotting one smirking, pasty-faced teenager sitting in the sort of high chair normally reserved for tennis umpires, "they've given them megaphones."

"Hello everyone!" she shouted like we were interested. "Welcome to the London Olympics! And part of the deal is you having lots of fun!" She paused. "What are you going to have?" I smirked at this foolishness. But the crowd bellowed and cheered and generally expressed the thought that, yes indeed, it was going to have fun. Inside, I died a little.

Brilliant, I thought, I'm with the happy-clappy lot, probably out-of-towners, a rabble of drooling idiots desperate to "have fun".

By the time I was queuing to have my bag searched I was fuming. The Off-Pink Kids were telling jokes, geeing us up, asking us where we came from, and – get this – wanting to high-five us! And the punters were loving it.

Morons.

Just beyond the metal-detector arch were a couple of coppers with fuck-off Heckler & Koch MP5 9mm machine guns and automatic pistols on their hips. This wasn't the Underground, and I'm not Brazilian, but I know well enough not to show off in front of these guys. I pretended to ignore them. As I did, the bigger, meaner-looking copper broke into a grin and stooped to speak to the small child in front of me. "Where are you from, then?" The kid grinned back and told him. Actually smiled back and told him where he came from. Passing another policeman pogoing with some of the Off-Pink Kids, I realised I was having a breakdown. Helen loved it – but, then, she isn't really *from* London.

And so the afternoon continued. I took pleasure in sitting through a Mexican wave. Alas, it did nothing to dull the crowd's enthusiasm for three hours of people falling off a diving board.

When it was over, the crowds shuffled out in one jovial trudging clump. The Off-Pink Kids were still cheery and charming, smiling and dancing and saying goodnight, hoping we'd had a great time. "See you again," they said, in a friendly, open way that suggested they meant it. Halfway along the path to the station some of them had, for reasons only they knew, arranged themselves in a line to high-five us as we went past.

In my defence, I was trapped in the throng and couldn't avoid them. As my hand slapped theirs they smiled at me and said "cheers". It was all very difficult; I had to smile too.

I don't understand how it happened. Frankly, I find it all rather stressful. Londoners aren't really built to be chirpy in crowds. And the revelation that these volunteer Games Makers of all shapes, sizes and ages, awkwardly dressed in that awful shade of pink, were only ever fun and helpful, took some time to sink in.

It's over now and I'm hoping that things will soon get back to normal.

It will get back to normal, won't it?

HOLIDAY

FIONA FLYNN

THE BIKE COP SIDLES UP to me
for zipping across a red light on
Shaftesbury Avenue. He looks as
reluctant about the situation as I feel.

Please don't give me a fine, I wail,
*not a fine. I'm sorry, but please don't
charge me thirty quid.*

Give me one good reason why not,
he says. *It's a daft thing to do and
there are dangerous drivers out there.*

Because it's the holidays?

He pauses. On the pavement beside us,
two middle-aged Dutchmen walk past,
a single orange flag draped around
their shoulders.

Go on then. But don't do it again.

Two hours later I'm back the other way,
but this time I wait at the lights, arms
crossed like a petulant fifth-former.
The cop's yellow vizzie gives him away
as he faces me on the opposite side
of the junction and, when he sees me,
he nods an acknowledgement of my
compliance. I blush and look the other
way, trying to hide my delight.

opposite: *the biggest McDonald's in the
world now has an outdoor seating area*

141

We've Lost Tom Cruise's Hands!

an Olympic Ambassador
in Leicester Square

Rebecca Thomas

Excuse me, but could you tell us if we're going in the wrong direction for Covent Garden?

The public toilets were supposed to be open for the Olympics but they're not, I'm afraid. You can use McDonald's – or the National Gallery, if you don't fancy that.

M&M's World – where is it? We were told it was near here! Oh, thank God.

He can't stay there – he'll be blocking the red carpet.

The zebra crossing! You know, the Beatles zebra crossing!

Would you like me to take a picture of you all together, with Wenlock? Let me just put these maps down.

We want to go to the museums. We've taken our cat to be spayed at Battersea and wanted to make a day of it.

To your left, towards the clock – see the Swiss clock? Then go right, and right again, and you'll see all the lanterns. That's Chinatown.

We need to be at Heathrow two hours ago – can we make it?

Mamma Mia? Straight ahead, you can't miss it.

Where are Tom Cruise's hands? We've walked all around and can't find them anywhere. They're in my book but they're not here!

Changing the guard? You've got twenty minutes and, unless you're a very fast walker, I don't think you're going to make it.

I'm very sorry to bother you, but please may I ask you a question?

See that little building, past the fountain in the middle? No, there – see it? With the queue? It's the only place we're allowed to recommend. Don't worry, it's a fast-moving queue.

Where's TK Maxx? Would you like some M&Ms?

Do you know where you're going? Do you know where you are?

Just wondering, is there any chance we can get into the Olympic Park?

Flowers David Fell

MY RECENTLY WIDOWED MOTHER stood among the flowers. "This is the best day I've had in years," she said.

He had had cancer. It took ages.

She did not mind that the flowers were a contrivance here in the Olympic Park, and surrounded by buildings posted with corporate messages. Neither did she mind that she had joined the painfully ignorant people that she had condemned only a few moments before, people who had ignored the "forbidden" signs and merrily tramped over the beautiful flowers.

She tramped, and she was happy, and it was the least she deserved. Somewhere nearby, someone jumped and ran and threw; here, my recently widowed mum smiled, a real smile, for the first time in years.

They really were very lovely flowers.

Waiting for Wenlock

Andrew Gray

Alex
Farebrother
-Naylor

"WILL YOU BE LUCKY ENOUGH TO MEET WENLOCK?" asked the pink London 2012 sign in a far corner of the Olympic Park. Good question. I'd been trying to meet him for a week and a half.

On the first Sunday of the Games, I was under strict instructions from the children of a friend to get pictures of Wenlock and Mandeville. But, as I trudged in the rain past corporate pavilions, meadows and works of art, I found not so much as a mascot dropping.

This struck me as something of a poor show. Mandeville, I could forgive – this wasn't really his gig. But Wenlock? What could explain *his* non-appearance? Was he ill? Did union rules prevent him from working weekends? Had he been the victim of an al-Qaeda kidnap plot? Very possibly. Another friend claimed to have spotted him in the Park the day after my visit, but that proved nothing: maybe his captors had let him out for a few hours to put us off the scent. Or maybe Lord Coe had pulled on a Wenlock suit and run around madly for a few hours, just to get a break from all the questions about empty seats.

I didn't see him at the Olympic football tournament at Wembley, or at the women's basketball, or in the entire Olympic Park on my next visit. For days, I scoured Flickr streams, Twitter feeds, websites and television pictures – and found no trace. I began to feel distinctly let down.

And then, after days of invisibility, there he suddenly was, prancing around the Olympic Stadium on prime-time TV as Britain won three golds on Super Saturday. He was there the next day too, cavorting with Usain Bolt. Across the whole weekend, Golden Wenlocks were thrust into the hands of Olympic champions. Finally, regretfully, I could reach only one conclusion: Wenlock was a glory-hunting prima donna, a shameless showboater – with an agent who had clearly done the mother of all deals on image rights.

Wenlock even took to Twitter to boast about his exploits with Bolt. A fan responded by asking if he would be at the canoe slalom. His answer was no surprise to me – snooty silence. I knew he would be staring at his phone in indignant disbelief, thinking: "Canoe slalom? Are you having a laugh? I don't get out of bed for a TV audience of less than twenty million."

I resolved to take a stand. Someone had to track Wenlock down and hold him to account. On a final visit to Stratford, my friend led me to the spot where he had been seen previously: a grassy area at the farthest edge of the Park. With a stage, and a pink sign announcing that Wenlock would soon make an appearance.

I waited.

Being a celebrity, Wenlock did not turn up on time. He was a whole fifteen minutes late. And, even then, he sent his personal assistant, a charming woman named Bianca, on to the stage first, to whip the crowd of youngsters into a frenzy before he himself deigned to appear and perform a "comedy" judo routine.

While children queued to have their photos taken with Wenlock, I challenged Bianca about his elusiveness. Bianca pleasantly pointed out that the sign stated clearly where and when he could be found each day. I boldly suggested that if Wenlock had tweeted his appearance details in advance, more people would know how to find him. Belligerently, I even questioned whether Wenlock was actually running his own Twitter feed, as his paws did not seem well suited to mobile phone keypads. Unruffled, Bianca calmly explained that "no one of any importance" handled their own Twitter account.

Suddenly, strangely, disconcertingly, I felt the burning sense of injustice that had driven me to this point begin to ebb. Perhaps the magnetic personality that had made Wenlock such a show business success was having its effect. I recalled his difficult childhood as a blob of molten metal in Bolton, and his brave decision to seek a better life elsewhere. As mascot for a city of bonus-trousering bankers and expenses-fiddling politicians, could he really be blamed for trying to cash in on his status?

As the sun slipped below the stadium roof that glorious evening, child after child hugged Wenlock and beamed at getting a picture with him. I began to feel ashamed and not a little ridiculous. Who was I to ruin this special moment? And when I finally came eye-to-camera with Wenlock, I sensed that behind the publicity-seeking façade was a sensitive soul whose overwhelming desire was to make people happy. I felt the Olympic Spirit envelop me completely, and shook his paw to seal our reconciliation. Some may allege that I even joined him in a Bolt-style celebration. But photographic evidence of any such shenanigans will, I'm afraid, remain even harder to find than Wenlock was.

20 minute queue for
£8 franchise hot dog

Outside Blackhorse Road, the bikes have
turned orange. On Walthamstow Marshes,
the fields have turned orange too.
Metal frames and canvas tents glow in
woozy tangerine, decorated with marigolds,
fresh imports from the Netherlands.

Through the gates come the Dutch sports fans.
Yes – they are also head-to-toe in orange.
They unchain their two-wheelers, mount,
and disappear off towards the south, a citrussy
parade of satsumas, apricots and clementines.

JUDE ROGERS

AFTER THE SUMMER

ROBIN PARKER

Before the summer, the boy didn't care about sport. Especially sport of the competitive kind. He'd always had the heartbreaking conviction that he was not the best at anything. With the stubbornness of a child he thought, well, if you can't do something in the best way, right away, then what's the point?

But he'd been primed at school, and among his peers, for an exciting global event happening in his own backyard. So he stood dutifully on the street for the torch relay, and grabbed a cheap flag to wave with one hand, only to let an ice cream drop from the other. His picture-perfect moment was ruined as he scrabbled around tearfully for any edible pieces. The flame-carrier whizzed past; the boy was wet-eyed and oblivious.

The near-constant presence of sports on TV in a normally non-sporty household proved both a novelty and an irritation. The boy had to bargain hard to watch "his" programmes, particularly in the hour before bedtime – or, as he called it, the *Scooby Doo* hour. He bought a lot of extra evening minutes as he ended up watching both. His time away from bed was also gradually getting stretched out by impromptu lounge-floor gymnastics demonstrations.

The boy started to like things. He liked diving. Gymnastics. Swimming. The shorter athletic sprints. But, better still, he liked awarding hypothetical bronzes, silvers and golds in arbitrary household competitions. His races to the end of the street also had sudden purpose. The binary of winning and not-winning was the easiest concept for him to grasp; what was less clear to him was when the win actually came. Half an hour into the diving semi-final, when Tom Daley and his rivals were undergoing a seemingly never-ending series of rounds, the boy had to admit defeat. "Tell me who won tomorrow," he said, as his head hit the pillow.

And then came the boy's attempts to be a TV presenter, improvising his own commentary. "Yay, this one's my favourite, he's going to win gold… actually, this one is." And the joy he felt backing someone because he liked their name, such as Chinese trampolinist Dong Dong. Slowly, but surely, the excitement that Team GB was the one team worth cheering for sunk in.

And then came the proof that, yes, the Games were a live spectacle happening right here in London. The boy saw Olympic riding in Greenwich and shooting in Woolwich. He saw Paralympic table tennis, basketball and powerlifting. His excitement was palpable, his delight at friendly soldiers ushering him in – with guns – slightly tinged with bemusement, his cheers at any Team GB effort infectious.

But these were not sports he chose to see, or understood, and no amount of sweet treats could curb his ambiguous relationship with all this strangeness. Was this it now? Would the Olympics always be happening in London? And would people keep banging on about them, Daddy?

I was seven when the Los Angeles Olympics happened. It came at the right time for me; for my boyish enthusiasm, if not ability, for basic PE. Daley Thompson, Seb Coe, Tessa Sanderson, Carl Lewis, Zola Budd… I followed the action on a tiny telly in a caravan in France, after each afternoon at the pool, savouring every minute.

I parted ways with the Olympics after that. I blame a dwindling interest in sport, and increasing demands on my time. Also, I've realised it's something else too – the way that age always slightly unravels who you once were.

But that interest came back this summer, all right. As I watched another boy, my five-year-old, run in his turn.

You Sane Bolt @yousanebolt
Thanks to all my fans. I'm now a
living legend for sure!
9 Aug 23:01

You Sane Bolt @yousanebolt
Going to get out of the digs.
Who's comin'?
9 Aug 23:01

You Sane Bolt @yousanebolt
Check it - an "English bus"
#69 #heyladiees
#whatswalthamstow
9 Aug 23:32

You Sane Bolt @yousanebolt
I'm out - this Ale is REAL
#notguinness
10 Aug 00:02

You Sane Bolt @yousanebolt
Hey Leyton Girl!!!!! What is
"pop-up"?
10 Aug 00:19

You Sane Bolt @yousanebolt
Check out my men Sam + Dave
at KEBABISH!!!!
#knobhead
10 Aug 01:29

You Sane Bolt @yousanebolt
BEER
10 Aug 01:52

You Sane Bolt @yousanebolt
i was lost but now i'm FOUND
at my main football GROUND.
enuff this running shit #brokenin
#saynuthin
10 Aug 02:04

You Sane Bolt @yousanebolt
This Emirates mighty small
- can of Lech my BALL
#leytonminimarket
#goooaal
10 Aug 02:19

You Sane Bolt @yousanebolt
PartyPoker? This ain't
dope #donttellbransonman
#whereisarsene
10 Aug 02:12

You Sane Bolt @yousanebolt
Now in CHANGING room!!!
#signthebolt #druuuuuunk
10 Aug 02:28

You Sane Bolt @yousanebolt
oh
10 Aug 02:41

You Sane Bolt @yousanebolt
I've found an animals head... oh
god #alewasnotreal #siiiiiick
10 Aug 02:49

You Sane Bolt @yousanebolt
I've put it on. The Lech's in front
of the goal. I can't see throug this
mask man #agggggggh
10 Aug 02:53

You Sane Bolt @yousanebolt
I'm wanderin. Dude just called
me Theo. WHERE AM I
##whatisawyvern
10 Aug 03:21

You Sane Bolt @yousanebolt
Grass, man - ohhhhhhmydayyys
#sickinanimalhead
10 Aug 04:21

You Sane Bolt @yousanebolt
Woke up in a maze. Head gone.
Magic come - 69 bus - Leyton
GIRL!! #coronationgardenscleaner
#usavedmylife
10 Aug 07:21

You Sane Bolt @yousanebolt
Just ran 4x100 relay practice
in 9.4 seconds! #sweeet
#poweroftheorient #zzzzz
10 Aug 10:00

... feverish passion;
patriotic fervour;
bubble, a fried slice,
and a choice of
tea or coffee...

Woolwich 2012.

Somewhere between Highbury and Dalston Kingsland, she thinks: if only I'd not always bunked off games on Wednesday afternoons. And somewhere between Walthamstow Central and Brixton, a transport controller hides her sad eyes with her hands and thinks: if only I'd prescribed egg-white omelettes, protein shakes and leg stretches before rush hour…

IN VICTORIA PARK

Every morning, usually near the bathing ponds, the Britannia pub or the bandstand, I'd see the blur. Bodies flying past, followed by joggers. I knew they were athletes as they all had their accreditations across their bodies, squares of plastic flapping as their limbs moved them forwards, effortlessly.

One morning, two runners sprinted past my bike and I thought I vaguely recognised one of them, but didn't have time to fumble for my camera. It wasn't until I saw him break the 800m world record that I realised it had been David Rudisha of Kenya.

ALEX MURRAY

THE BOY WHO CAME TO LONDON

We're in a huge bowl. We're little flecks. We're waiting to see them emerge from the tunnel on the far side of the bowl, tiny dots that will bring splashes of bright colour to the dark orange surface. To one side of me are two teenage brothers. To the other, a grey-haired man wearing a Yes T-shirt. Next to him, a mum and dad and two little girls. Behind me, a couple kissing, their faces painted smudgy red, white and blue. I'm a fleck on my own, knowing no one, not a soul. But, when I see him, jogging around the oval, I know him straight away. In his tracksuit top, he looks tiny, like a boy. His long arms and legs look like matchsticks, skinny and snappable. But then, as he comes closer to us, I see the strength inside them.

As he passes, he waves. The bowl bubbles, lifts, erupts.

Five minutes later, it's time. The runners slot themselves between the bright white lines. Coloured vests and names in heavy letters shimmer off the huge screens. I see him up there too, rendered in millions of tiny, glowing pixels. I could just watch him that way, as I've watched so many other athletes before, following the camera's tracking gaze.

For a moment, I'm out of the bowl. Away from the brothers, the prog fan, the family, the tricoloured lovers. It's 1991, and I'm thirteen years old. My nose is pressed up against a much smaller screen, watching world athletics for the very first time.

That year was the year that this boy came to London, the place his father came from. He was eight then. The tracking gaze closes in on his huge brown eyes.

Before the starting mark, the boy he was, the man he is, arches his back. I look away from the screen. There he is: one tiny fleck. His city holds its breath, all together.

Bang.

We're in a huge bowl. Eighty thousand little flecks rise and fall. A loop, then another, another, another. Fifteen sets of muscles tense and pulse under taut skin. My eyes dash between the pixels and the person I want to see on the track, between my past and our present. On the screen, what's happening looks like a Hollywood thriller; dramatic, dreamy and wonderful. In reality, the magic takes a different form. This figure that keeps circling, circling, circling, getting smaller, and then bigger, is flesh, bones and blood. And so am I.

As eleven minutes pass, he breaks through his barrier, breaks from the pack. The bowl has a new pulse, a new spirit, a heartbeat of its own. On the last circuit, our row rises, every fleck joined together, teenage screams, flailing grey hair, two little girls jumping on white plastic seats, as we watch the boy's strides, arms, eyes and mouth widen.

Mo turns towards us one last time, and London gains a new shape. I look around, at the people standing next to me – realer than real, somehow larger than life. Every tiny fleck is suddenly filled with significance. This is what I want London to always mean to me.

JUDE ROGERS

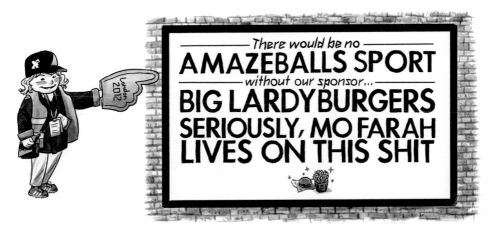

Alex
Farebrother
-Naylor

Chris looked at Alex and Alex looked at Chris.

"What the hell is that?" said Alex.

Chris grinned sheepishly.

"A bicycle? Since when have you been interested in bicycles? And how much did it cost?"

"I don't expect you to pay for it," Chris murmured.

"Too bloody right. But that's not the point. We're supposed to be cutting back, and then you come home with tha… oh, we'll talk about it later. The ceremony's about to start. And you're not making me watch this one on sodding iPlayer."

As Chris reached out for the TV remote, the sleeve of the pale blue T-shirt rode up, revealing, under the protective cling film, just above the bicycle, a familiar sideburned face.

Alex sighed. It was a good job he loved her.

Sankt Andreas Hotel
Düsseldorf

Is that Freddie Mercury?
On the TV? In the
corner beside the bar?
Isn't he dead?

GO HOME AND SWITCH ON BBC ONE

Dale Lately

"You will *not* be able to see the end of the Olympics on this screen," booms the steward in the red coat to the crowds beneath the giant M&S logo. "Anyone wanting to watch the end of the Olympics has to go elsewhere."

Evidently the screen has better things to show the residents of Stratford right now than the ceremonies taking place in the gigantic spaceship just beyond Yo! Sushi. Right now, it's serving the viewing needs of the local community by depicting a spinning Powerade bottle.

"Hydrating the athletes!" it boasts.

Although pretty much all you can do at the Stratford gate is turn up in order to be told to go home again, a surprisingly large number of people have turned up in order to be told to go home again. Beneath the weird fifty-foot steel tree sculptures, primary-coloured crowds swish around, crashing against the human barriers. Servicemen in yellow coats chat and cadge fags. An Islamic march, chaperoned by police, is protesting against the evils of modern society. Alongside, a Christian group, banging on drums, is protesting against the evils of modern society. Everybody else seems to be too busy getting on with enjoying the evils of modern society to listen.

"Gillette!" beams the side of a nearby tower block. "Nothing beats a great start."

A millenarian feel is in the air: people are shouting, raging, chanting, advertising. Spotting what I think is a PlayStation promotion, I approach a bunch of guys with *Is Life Just a Game?* emblazoned on their yellow T-shirts. It turns out to be a Muslim community group from Tower Hamlets eager to tell me about the Qur'an.

"Check out the website," one of them says.

"Yeah, I'll… thanks."

"There's a lot more information on the website."

More and more people are massing at the gate.

One of the stewards – a young Asian guy, east London to judge from his accent – has a loudhailer. "Please go home," he says. "If you want to watch the Closing Ceremony, go home and switch on BBC One."

He intones the words wearily, as if he thinks his soul might actually collapse if he has to repeat them one more time. I feel a pang of sympathy for him, and for the wobbly human wall behind him: big bouncer-like Poles in security jackets, gum-chewing young women, crew-cuts in shades examining mobiles. Further back stands a platoon of bored cops, arms folded, checking texts, yawning into fists.

The Muslim community group are now taking cameraphone snaps of each other.

"What does God mean to you?" someone keeps asking. "What does he mean to *you*?"

"Good people of Stratford," another steward is saying through his megaphone, "it will be in your interests to disperse. You can watch the ceremony live on your TV."

A couple of uniformed soldiers are now posing for a picture with the Qur'an guys, one of whom holds up a copy of the book to ensure it makes it into the photo.

I wander into Stratford itself, that formerly run-down corner of Newham which, since the Games came, has magically transformed itself into a run-down corner of Newham with a big stadium beside it. I've heard a lot about the regeneration legacy – it's why we now have a huge motorway bordered by Tetris cubes with incredibly expensive flats inside – and here it is in action: it's 10 p.m., yet the local Poundland is still doing a roaring trade, and Burger King, McDonald's and the kebab shops are packed to bursting. I try to get into a small park to watch the ceremony on the big TV screen, but am told it's already full of people trying to watch the ceremony on the big TV screen. Wandering down the street, I gaze up at the glazed cliff of one of the new Tetris blocks. The flats are still furnitureless, empty, and giant TO LET signs are pasted on the side.

"Thank you for visiting Newham, London," a sign proclaims. "A place where people choose to live, work and stay."

On a crap bit of road near the Bow flyover, a small crowd is squinting into the distance at the fireworks going off over the stadium. I join them.

When floodlit orange and purple smoke begins to drift out through the laser lights, I assume the ceremony has probably finished, and cut back towards the gates. People are flooding out. There's something jubilant about the scene – songs, jumbled cheers, red-coated young stewards laughing and joking with each other. Somehow, it looks more like a staff get-together at Carphone Warehouse than a security force.

As I head towards the station, I pass the Christian group, still banging on their drums, still protesting against the evils of modern society beneath the glow of the giant M&S – though a couple of them have evidently got a bit tired, and are sharing a fag, while another stops to take a swig of Diet Pepsi before picking up her *Christ is Redeemed* sign and joining back in with the singing.

In the middle of the seething station, a big mural shows happy, sporty people of all colours peacefully co-existing beside an advertisement for Lloyds TSB.

And then a fortnight passes. You can feel the lull… luuuull… luuuuull… but there's a tension in those vowels. Something is happening. Tickets will be easy to get, surely… oh. They've all gone. It'll be as quiet it was during the Olympi… oh. Real life and the crowds swirl together. And then a man called Stephen sits in the middle of the stadium, and tells us to look up at the stars and not down at our feet. To try to make sense of everything. It's hard not to.

Her Name Is Rio

East London in early September. It feels like a hot summer night, but it's getting dark at last. Three Brazilian women are screeching with delight.

They're not wearing very much, and each is being carried in the arms of a tall strapping man, cuddling up to him, placing kisses on his cheek.

The men lift their girls up, and stand them on a platform. Then the music starts, three notes – dah, dah, DAH! Ten metres away are poles stretching high into the air. Up them start to rise green rectangles of cloth decorated with yellow diamonds and blue starry globes.

The trumpets diddle-diddle-um. Diddle-diddle-um. The three women are alone now. The one in the middle is crying, her eyes closed. She can't see the flags, or the stadium around her. But, earlier on, she touched her male guide to help her stay in her lane, heard the crowd scream, and sensed the world looking at her in a new way.

Jude Rogers

80,000 Silences

Jude Rogers

Silence.

Baton.

Silence.

Baton.

If a feather fell now, and landed on the track,
80,000 people would hear its barbs brush the rubber.

Baton.

After the men without arms and legs ran, after the
women in wheelchairs sprinted, everyone listened to the
announcer's request for quiet, for the blind relay teams to
be allowed to move their bodies in silence, for nothing to
distract them out of their lanes until after the last baton
had been passed.

Baton.

Sound waves, filaments, nerve endings.

SOUND.

*Scene: a pop-up pub on Leyton High Road. It is 9th September, 2012.
Two men in their twenties sit at a small table, on two mismatched chairs,
holding pints of real ale.*

SAM: Bloody hell, look at her, Dave. She's sixty fucking feet in the air!

DAVE: Sam!

SAM: What?

DAVE: *[whispering]* Keep your voice DOWN, you knob-head,
for God's sake.

SAM: What's her name, Dave? Rhian? Is she Welsh?

DAVE: *[shaking head wearily]* It's Rihanna, you idiot. She's that pop star
who sings about her umbrella.

SAM: So why's she on a throne in the Olympic Stadium, then?

DAVE: *[putting head on table, one hand still holding his pint, and talking
to floor]* She doesn't have one at all times, Sam. And she has other
songs. Pop stars usually do.

SAM: *[also putting head under table]* What you doing, Dave?

DAVE: Texting Jana. "Oh, Jana, take me away to Prague with you for
some Staropramen."

SAM: Text that funny bloke who broke into the Orient ground too.
Tall fella. Bloody fast, innit?

*A minute passes in the Paralympic Closing Ceremony. Rihanna sings
while being winched across the Olympic Stadium on a red-cushioned
throne. Dave puts his phone in his pocket and lifts his head, wearily.
Sam's mouth is wide open, goldfish-style.*

SAM: What's she singing? We found what?

DAVE: *[sighing]* We found love. That's the name of her song.
It's been playing out of every car window from Walthamstow
to Canning Town all bloody summer. "We found love in a
hopeless place."

SAM: *[suddenly bursting into laughter]* Ha-ha-ha-ha! That figures,
don't it?

DAVE: What?

SAM: That she found love in a hopeless place.

DAVE: *[sighing deeply and resting head on table again]* Why, Sam?

SAM: Come on, Dave. Surely even world travellers like you have been
to fucking Stratford.

You know what I really miss?
Seeing the Russian paralympic
squad having their breakfast smoke
outside Café Rouge every morning
when I go to buy the paper.

IAIN STARED GLUMLY across the stained formica.

"It's like I was telling the sculptor Rachel Whiteread, Will, when I was explaining to her how Hackney's pre-Games decontamination and realignment into a fugitive cartography of designer lock-ups and guerilla sofa bars had created a hallucinatory Ballardian nexus of dystopian interzones and put me right off the idea of getting a cat, some of the ley lines they dug up to build the Basketball Arena had been there since the days of King Lud." He paused. "Look, I drew her a map."

Iain passed Will a piece of paper. It was a menu from a Turkish cafe in Dalston, covered in biro scrawl, and with a small piece of what looked like chargrilled aubergine stuck to one corner. Will pulled a face.

"Are those conduplicated testicular orbs with an intermedial indurated intromittent organ extravasating prostatic fluid?"

"A spunking cock and balls? Yes. I think she must have drawn them when I wasn't looking. There are more all over the back, look. I think she gets a bit frustrated, just filling the negative spaces inside objects with concrete in order to make people think twice about things."

"Hmmm," said Will, slipping the menu into his pocket. "So, tell me: what tactical methodology do you advocate that we implement as a counterpoising praxis?"

"What do I think we should do about it? Well, I suppose we could try walking around something. Like the M25, or the Olympic Pa…"

"Can you execute an intramental reinstauration of the inimical predicament that eventuated when you essayed an experimental circumambulation of Peter Ackroyd?"

"Do I remember what happened when I tried to walk round Peter Ackroyd? Of course I do." Iain paused. "He didn't like it, did he?"

"He articulated his grievances to the constabulatory functionaries."

"He called the police, yes. But it was taking much longer than I'd anticipated." Iain leant forwards, dropped his voice to a whisper, and gripped the plastic ketchup bottle on the table in front of him with both hands. "I actually wondered afterwards whether – " he slowly rotated the rotund red receptacle between his palms – "he might have been turning round."

Will gazed out through the steamy, net-curtained window.

"I suppose," he said at last, "we just have to accept that it was all a lot of fun, and most people enjoyed it."

Iain stared at him.

"I'm sorry," he said, "I'm not sure I understand what you mean."

Iain and Will have a Cup of Tea (by Matt Haynes)

YOU REMEMBER PICTURES OF EAST BERLIN, DON'T YOU? It looks a bit like that. A closed, empty pub, sitting on a silent, grey road. Tall towers of housing rising behind it, reaching up towards a solid sky.

If you notice the white road signs outside the pub, just before you come to the mini roundabout, you'll see that they say *Look Left*. You can't do anything *but* look now. Look left, and you see a road blocked off by a red and white barrier. You can't access the tall towers beyond it, not without someone letting you pass. One day soon, you will be able to cross the line, and things will be different then, or so they say. But, for the meantime, you're not allowed.

A pub has stood on this site since 1855. This one was built in the late 1960s in pale, heavy brick, with a reddish-brown roof sitting demurely on top. The windows are latticed to suggest old-fashioned bonhomie. Blackboards still promise pool and live music in faded, garish chalk. But the only sound you hear is the whoosh of tumbleweed.

Wheeler's stood at the gateway to the greatest show on earth. It still does. The flats behind it are now the East Village, emblems of a brave new world, all clean and safe and pure. But, here on Leyton Road, the memories of something else linger. The loud music that used to play until the early hours, the shouting and the swearing, the barmaids flaunting their nipples, the used condoms and the broken bottles, the lost souls emerging from a dank, dirty maw of a door at five in the morning.

Pull back, adjust the lens, and you see a new picture. But, in this scene, in grimy close-up, Stratford's edgelands still pulse.

JUDE ROGERS

"These riverside apartments," says the brochure, "offer a sophisticated and stylish contemporary living space in one of the most scenic areas of east London." Matchmakers Wharf, they've called it, but nobody ever made matches here. They made cars. Beautiful, die-cast metal cars so small they could fit in a matchbox...

REPORT ON THE EIGHTH PSYCHOGEOGRAPHICAL OLYMPIAD, LONDON, OCTOBER 2012

CHRIS ROBERTS

The first Psychogeographical Olympiad was organised in Paris by the Dadaists in 1920, with four-yearly contests following in Zurich (1924), Athens (1928), Montevideo (1932) and Antwerp (1936). There was a revival by the Situationists in 1964, again in Paris, and a rather shambolic event in San Francisco in 1968. The latest resurrection of the idea by the Disorganising Committee of the London Psychogeographical Drift occurred when members saw the proposed mascots for London 2012 and realised surrealism had lost its way.

Controversy dogged the 2012 event from the start, culminating in the German team setting up its own London Psychogeographical Games in a park just off Weinerstrasse in Berlin 36; in mitigation, they explained that walking the streets of contemporary Berlin using a nineteenth-century map of London was the very essence of the discipline. Most of the world, though, was in London, to celebrate something that — to attempt to paraphrase Will Self — is not about maps, but the feel of an area's streets, and the interplay of past and present associations. Speaking of Mr Self, the London Disorganising Committee recognised his status by introducing to their games the Selfathlon, in which a simple sentence had to be reconstructed using the most obscure words possible. Surprisingly, the contest was won by the Icelandic team — their only gold in the games — who bravely turned the

nine-word, thirteen-syllable phrase "London
is a big place full of interesting things"
into a fifty-seven-word, four-hundred-syllable
monster. "This gallimaufrymous Nebuchadnezzar
of topographical splendours and a polysexual
pantheon of statuary..." it began. As expected,
the home side did rather well in most of the
water-based events on London's hidden rivers
and lost waterways, though the coveted Unlikely
Historical Re-enactment gold went to the
Chinese for their reconstruction of the last
days of the Graf Spee using Deptford Creek as
the River Plate. The rowing team, based on the
canal at Broadway Market, covered themselves
in individual and team glory with a series of
rows about the merits of Dalston vis-a-vis
Brixton Village and the superiority of North
London over South London in general. Team GB
also won gold in the Decathlon; starting at
Dr Johnson's House, they linked ten London cats
to finish at St Michael Paternoster a full three
minutes ahead of the much-fancied French mob,
who pitched up on the South Bank at the Coade
Stone Lion. The Belgians, meanwhile, won the
HepCatAthlon with their jazz walk of Soho, and
- perhaps unsurprisingly - the Irish team's
only gold came in the Poguathon, in which
they broke the record for crossing the city
using only the lyrics of Pogues' songs. There
were further medals for team GB in Walking
Self-Importantly In Circles Around Things and
in two of the five so-called "drift marathons"
- long ambles across London on the vague off
chance of seeing something. The much shorter
White City Estate Dog-Walking Drift, won by the
Canadians with a dachshund named Emily, was
one of a number of events which took place at
former Olympic venues. The swimming, which was

held at Finchley Road Baths, in the car park, was not among them.

There was success for the Americans in many of the equestrian events, but disappointment in the dressage, where their much fancied team of skinheads strolling around Mile End finished fifth. In part this was due to a strong performance from the Brazilian punks who flaneured flamboyantly around the King's Road, but even they were pipped for third place by Zaire's Strand-based Mohawks. Silver went to a pack of Australian Sloane Rangers, whilst the unfancied home team grabbed gold with their studied recreation of favoured Macaroni strolls in Bloomsbury and Piccadilly.

The Walking To Make A Rude Gesture On The Landscape Of The City produced an unplanned shock when the gold was snatched by a Serbian team whose "one finger salute" on a vertical walk up the Gherkin greatly impressed the judges. Another surprise occurred during the Looting In Reverse, with the Japanese dropping off the most sportswear in the agreed time across a series of outlets in Tottenham. Unfortunately, police action prevented their attendance at the medal ceremony.

As the flag of the ancient kingdom of the East Saxons was lowered for the last time, and the teams exited the stadium using their national walks, a disorganising spokesperson said they hoped that they had set the standard for future games. She added, when pressed, that she had most enjoyed the Cycling East Dulwich Using A Map Of Clapham and the Stride Somewhere Beautiful events.

... and then,
after the
last horse
had passed,
London was
carefully put
away until
next time...

BORIS AND THE BANSHEES *by* Thomas McColl

According to Radio Kent, the last person to see Boris Johnson alive was Arthur Culpepper, a retired postman from Gravesend, who'd been walking his dog Trevor along the river at the time. Mr Culpepper, however, remains unsure: his initial thought, he reminds everyone who asks, had been simply that it was a very odd sort of design for a kite.

From my bedroom, in a block that now overlooks the Olympic Stadium, I'd often watch the banshees trying to straighten out their tangled hair with silver combs. They'd sit in a shallow ditch right beside the railway track, and I'd feel sorry for them, forced to comb their hair again each time a train from Hackney Wick went by on its way to Stratford. But then I looked up "banshees" on Google and found out they're always combing their hair, no matter what.

Still, the one thing everyone knows about a banshee is that you don't cross a banshee. Everyone, it turned out, except the Olympics people. Being outsiders, they didn't even know that we *had* banshees in east London; we locals could have told them – warned them – but they were hardly going to start listening to people they'd deliberately ignored for years, people whose lives were now being blighted by the massive construction site, by the constant noise and dust, by the works going on all day and sometimes into the night.

It's one thing messing locals around, though. Banshees – that's another matter altogether.

Eileen, who chairs our residents' association, is known as someone who can talk to the dead – she's in great demand for séances all over Hackney. At a residents' association meeting in the summer of 2011, she'd told us it was easier getting a response from the other world than it was from any Olympics official, and we'd laughed, albeit cheerlessly. Then she'd told us she did have *some* good news, however, as she'd spoken to the banshees – as she often did, apparently, when she went out on her late-night walks – and they'd told her all about Ardal or, more specifically, about their plan to assassinate Ardal when he came to Stratford to open the new Westfield Centre in September.

There was a pause while we digested this. I, for one, was very confused. Was Ardal O'Hanlon opening Westfield? Why would the banshees want to kill Father Dougal?

As I pondered their possible motives, Eileen added that she'd been assured by the banshees that if their plot to assassinate Ardal failed, they'd call on Clíodhna – their queen – for help.

"Clodna?" I said, hesitantly.

"No, Cli-odh-na," said Eileen, pronouncing the name slowly as if she was talking to a child.

Luckily Ted, who was sitting on my left – and who, having done an evening class in Irish folklore, often stepped in when Eileen hit us with some weird and confusing revelation via the banshees – was happy to give us all some background info.

Clíodhna, Ted explained, was originally a beautiful goddess who, having fallen in love with a mortal named Ciabhan, had herself become mortal in order to be with him. But, exhausted after swimming to his village on the south coast of Ireland from her home on the otherworldly island of Tir Tairngire, she'd fallen asleep on the harbour wall and promptly been swept back out to sea by a great wave.

"So… she died?" I was more confused than ever.

"No," said Eileen. "Being a former goddess, she lived on in a castle beneath the waves as queen of the banshees. And now, whenever the banshees face a threat from someone who is out to avenge an ancient curse, she returns in the form of a seabird, flying above the waves."

"So… she helps the banshees when they're in trouble?"

"Not just banshees," said Ted. "Mortals too. Like Cormac Laidir MacCarthy."

"Caramac…?"

"Cormac Laidir MacCarthy," repeated Eileen, with just a hint of exasperation. "Cormac lived in the 15th century, a feudal Irish lord who, one day, as he was walking along the Cork shoreline, appealed to Clíodhna for assistance in a lawsuit he was fighting. Clíodhna, appearing to him as a huge seagull, told him to kiss the first stone he found on his way to court and, after doing as she'd said, he successfully pleaded his case with such great and unaccustomed eloquence that he decided to incorporate the stone into the parapet of the castle he was building at Blarney, with the promise that anyone who kissed it would become similarly silver-tongued.

"One man to do so," Eileen continued before we could stop her, "was Ardal O'Brien, a chieftain who rose to power in south-east Ireland in 1508. Ardal was extremely proud of his beautiful blonde hair; people said he spent even more time combing his locks than the banshee who sat in the ditch at the side of the track that led to his castle did hers. The banshee had a comb of pure, shining silver and, when Ardal saw how wonderfully straight her hair was, and how beautifully it gleamed in the moonlight, he ordered one of his soldiers to steal it. The soldier succeeded, but the banshee cursed the terrified chieftain, screeching that Ardal would never be able to use any comb ever again. From that moment on, every comb that Ardal picked up crumbled to dust. His blonde hair became tangled and matted and, knowing that his subjects thought he'd let himself go, he lost his self-confidence, and made many bad decisions that brought the province to ruin. He was deposed and ended his life a poor pathetic beggar. His only consolation was the knowledge that not only is a banshee's curse always avenged exactly five hundred years after it is cast, but the victim will, once the curse is lifted, be even stronger than before. All Ardal had to do was wait five hundred years, however many lifetimes it took."

As soon as I got home from the meeting, I typed "Ardal O'Brien" into Google. All that came up, though, were dozens of LinkedIn and Facebook pages – and I quickly gave up the search as *X Factor* was coming on. The more I thought about it, though, the more I thought there might be something in it.

According to Ted, there had always been more banshees around Stratford than anywhere else in London. Not just because of the Irish connection – many Irish people had settled in the area, particularly towards Maryland and Ilford – but also because there was so much unused open space. For years, these lonely creatures had lived in the marshlands around Arena Fields and along each side of the mostly deserted and derelict Carpenter's Road. But then, after the success of the Olympic bid, everything had changed.

Very soon, the banshees' eyes were blood-red not from crying and screeching, but from the thick dust in the air. The noise of diggers meant they had to wail even louder just to be heard and, whenever they laid their heads down, trucks and cranes would start up like metal monsters waking; the poor banshees rarely got any sleep.

But that wasn't all. Soon, they started seeing, in discarded newspapers, photos of Boris. Boris and his tousled blonde mop. And, when they did, they grew very scared indeed.

Boris Johnson had become Mayor of London in 2008, and his star had been rising ever since. It could rise all the way to No. 10, the papers claimed, for his gift of the gab – his blarney, as the Irish would say – seemed to be having the same effect on those in high places as it had already had on ordinary people in London. His charm and charisma knew no bounds. In fact, it seemed there was only one thing in the city he couldn't control: his haystack hair.

The banshees, of course, knew why that was. They also knew that he had to be stopped, before his terrifying, ever-growing power brought another province to ruin and made everyone's lives an absolute misery – especially their own for he would, they were sure, make a point of seeking out the one who had first cursed him, in order to exact revenge. So when they read in the papers that Boris would be opening the new Westfield, they hatched a plan.

Now, one other thing that everyone knows about a banshee is that a banshee's wail can be piercing enough to shatter glass. What's less well known is that, just as the British army has, so it says, perfected the art of precision bombing in Afghanistan and Iraq in order to avoid "collateral damage", so banshees have perfected the art of precision wailing: the ability to direct a scream at any window up to a mile away, and shatter it – or simply crack it enough to loosen it – without breaking neighbouring panes.

And, on 13th September, as Boris stood there in Westfield, running his hand through his tousled scruffy hair and telling the interviewer from LBC that the construction people had worked "flat out" to ensure that this church of shiny commerce provided a proper "gateway to the Olympics", a five-foot by two-foot-six glass ceiling tile plummeted thirty feet towards his head.

Whee

And shattered into a thousand pieces just yards from where he was standing.

It was close, but not close enough. The distraught banshees had failed not because they'd got their calculations wrong, though; it had happened because the dust in their lungs had affected the tone and timbre of their voices. Boris had, you could say, been saved by the Olympic Delivery Authority.

By the following summer, there were only a few banshees left around Stratford – the old crones I saw from my bedroom window, and a dozen more living on borrowed time in the last pockets of wasteland yet to be cleared by the machines. The rest had moved to Kent, where the air was clear, to wait amongst the reeds and ditches of the Thames Estuary for the return across the sea of their queen, Clíodhna. For, if nothing else, the incident at Westfield had proved that they could not defeat Boris alone.

By all accounts, Boris took the near miss in his stride. But he knew, all right – knew that the banshees were on to him. He also knew that if he didn't do whatever it took to destroy every last one of them then, with the help of Clíodhna, they would stop him achieving his revenge, the curse would not be lifted, his five-hundred-year wait for power would come to nothing, and his hair would still look awful.

And so, as the final touches were put to the Olympic Park, Boris plotted. And as the athletes arrived and the Games got under way, Boris plotted. At a fob-the-locals-off event in Victoria Park, he rode on a zip-wire and, when the ride stalled, dangled helplessly above the laughing crowds in a blue safety helmet; even as he dangled, though, grinning like Good Old Boris always grins, he was plotting, plotting, plotting.

When Eileen explained, at our next residents' association meeting, that Boris's plan to build a new airport on the Isle of Grain had less to do with easing congestion at Heathrow and Gatwick and more to do with his all-consuming quest to defeat the banshees, everything started to make sense; it explained why, for instance, ever since Westfield, Boris had been desperately lobbying the government to approve the building of an airport that would bury every last patch of marshland on the Hoo Peninsula under tarmac and concrete. He knew that time was running out.

He was confident, though, Eileen said sadly. The Games were over. The diggers had moved on. Hackney Wick was polished, filled-in, and banshee-free. Boris had his enemies where he wanted them: out on the Kent marshes, ready for the first drop of concrete to be poured.

It was at this point that Ted, who'd just popped out to the kitchen to check on the cricket scores, came back in and said that they were saying on the radio that Boris had gone missing.

"Missing?" said Eileen.

"Just taken off, apparently," Ted answered, shaking his head.

His body, of course, has never been recovered. Largely because no one has ever really known where to look. It's all there in the minutes of our residents' association meetings, under Any Other Business, but... as I said at the start, no one ever thinks to ask people like us. And, to be fair, we know about it only because one day, some weeks after it all happened, Eileen – standing at the very spot in Victoria Park where Boris stalled on his zip-wire – had been accosted by a large seagull with blood-red eyes that had swooped down, perched on her arm, spread its wings and let out a series of guttural shrieks.

"So... what did it say then, this bird?" demanded Ted. He was sitting between me and Eileen, and clearly impatient for her to get on with her tale.

"Well..." said Eileen.

And then she told us what Clíodhna had told her.

Boris, it seemed, had been at the top of his glass castle beside Tower Bridge, with its wail-proof windows slanted to face the sky, poring over the airport plans – *and*, Eileen suspected, cackling to himself at the thought of all the devastation that would be wrought. It would, he'd probably been thinking, mean destroying the habitat of many birds, but – that was a sacrifice Londoners should be prepared to make if they wanted to live in an international city...

... and a sacrifice he was certainly prepared to make to get rid of the banshees.

Suddenly, though, he'd sensed that the sky outside had darkened. And, when he'd looked up, he'd seen, through his floor-to-ceiling windows, thousands of seagulls, so many that the midday sun was totally obliterated, furiously swirling around City Hall.

Screeeeeeeeeeeeeeeeeeeeeeeeeeeeeeeeeeeech…

The birds had thudded against the glass. Cracks had begun to appear. There were just too many – the glass couldn't hold! Then it had shattered and Boris's office had been filled with the ear-splitting cries of the gulls and the howl of the wind.

Led by Clíodhna, the birds had swirled into a mini-tornado over the desk, their beaks furiously tearing the airport plans into tiny pieces which had, in turn, been swept up and out of the building by the wind and fallen like confetti on bemused Londoners below. Fearing that the gulls would tear next at his bird-nest hair, Boris had smashed open the display cabinet in which he'd been keeping various mayoral mementos and pulled out the famous blue safety helmet. He'd clearly hoped to use it to stop the birds grabbing at his locks, but the birds had been unfazed; they'd simply lifted him up by his jacket and carried him out through the broken window, out of his castle, and…

… out over the heads of passers-by who, hearing him yelling, had laughed and reached for their cameras.

"Look, it's Boris!"

"What an idiot!"

But then the mood had changed.

"I can't believe it – look at him, trying to pull off the same stunt again."

"Where's the zip-wire, though? I can't see a zip-wire."

And then it had changed again.

"Are we paying for this?"

The joke had worn so thin that it was no longer a joke at all.

And so Boris had been carried out to sea by an enormous flock of angry birds…

… who, Eileen assured us, wouldn't have let him go until he was way beyond the Hoo Peninsula.

If anybody cared to look.

THE END

CHASING

THE

SUNSET

TIM TURNER

CAUGHT BY THE WASH from passing traffic, the boat rocks up and down beside the jetty. Then, at last, the boatman uncoils the rope, and the skipper eases us out into smoother water. As we pass under Hungerford Bridge, I glance up at the commuters bustling across to Waterloo, and feel slightly smug.

At the height of the Great Olympic Travel Panic that gripped the city in the spring, the management at our firm had instructed us to research alternative means of getting to work should the public transport network grind to a halt, as it was widely expected to do. Living in Fulham, I was vaguely aware of a riverboat service, and now I took the trouble to try it out. It was a revelation. Journey time: same as the District Line. Stressfulness: a fraction of the District Line.

Our boat is old — a plaque on the cabin attests that it saw service at Dunkirk — but it seems to do all the stuff you might want a boat to do: float, move in the right direction, that kind of thing. We sit on blue plastic chairs, the sort they had in school assembly halls when I was a boy. There aren't many passengers, which makes me fear for the future of the service. Then again, it adds to the delicious feeling of being in on a secret.

The others read newspapers or iPads, or chat with their neighbours. I prefer to sit with my arm on the rail, letting the river breeze blow through me as I watch the scenery go by. The views of the Houses of Parliament and the London Eye are the best available, but I prefer the less sought-after sights. The tide is low this evening, exposing mysterious steps down to the water and strange dark holes where long-lost rivers run into the Thames. Wading birds gather on exposed mud banks on which houseboats squat, ropes taut, waiting for the tide to rise and refloat them.

Out here on the river, we are part of an unspoken brotherhood: the schoolchildren messing about in yachts and canoes in front of MI6 at Vauxhall; the men in business suits drinking and laughing on a pleasure boat; the glamorous couple in the speedboat that bumps messily past. As we pass under Chelsea Bridge, I hear a siren, and, looking back, see an ambulance race across to the north bank, then turn left along Chelsea Embankment. For a few moments its course runs parallel to ours, then it swings inland to attend some unknown emergency.

We chug steadily westwards, chasing the sunset.

Mouth of the Effra

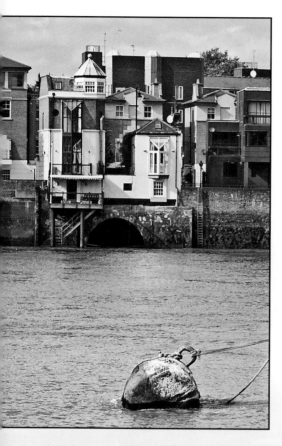

Mouth of the Tyburn

At Cadogan Pier the boatman does something wrong with the rope and we drift past the gap in the railings. No one can get off, and there's some good-natured teasing of the crew as they sort it out. Eventually, a handful of passengers disembark and head up the walkway. At low tide, it's so implausibly steep that it seems as if they ought to need ropes and crampons.

We nose out into the river again. On this early autumn evening the air is chilly, but not unpleasant. After a stressful day in front of a computer, this is exactly what I need. I breathe deeply and watch the sky ahead darkening. Next week I will be fifty. I try not to think about what that means.

In front of Lots Road Power Station is a row of yellow buoys, each with a single cormorant perched on top like a sentry. As we approach Chelsea Harbour, the skipper eases our boat over to the north bank. We moor, and I step out onto the pier.

Just before I return to everyday life, I pause at the top of the walkway and take one last look back at the river. In the soft grey light towards Wandsworth Bridge, the boat, our Dunkirk veteran, is already disappearing around the next bend.

Chasing the sunset.

Olympic Park Construction Site

British Waterway and towpath closed
No entry beyond this point

These passageways are under
C.C.T.V surveillance

For further information contact
Construction Hotline 0800 072 2110

Waterborne emergencies contact
0800 47 999 47

IN EARLY OCTOBER, Hong and I tried out the Olympic Park route Callum had told me about. From Canada Square, we ran through the lunchtime crowd flowing out into the Canary Wharf colonnades and made for the broad sweep of the Thames at Westferry. Here we turned inland, across Narrow Street and through Ropemakers Fields, to pick up the Limehouse Cut and head north-east to Bow Locks.

Dug in the 1760s to provide a direct route from the Lee Navigation to the Thames upriver of the Isle of Dogs that avoided the tortuous, tidal lower reaches of Bow Creek and the long haul around the island, the Limehouse Cut runs dead straight for most of its two miles, closely walled in on either side by the concrete, glass and London stock of restored Victorian warehouses, converted post-war factories, and new apartment blocks.

Hong and I were alone on the towpath; the Cut was eerily silent. At Bow Locks, we took the footbridge onto the central island and then crossed and re-crossed the waterway to continue north on the eastern bank of the Lee Navigation. We were now following little blue signs to the Olympic Park and shortly,

beyond the grassy embankment, we saw the Stadium looming up on the right, grey and still against the white sky. Closer by, rows of multi-storey modular buildings were being slowly disassembled.

As the Stadium slipped behind us and we headed on towards the junction with the Hertford Union, we spotted him up ahead: a young, bearded man, bending down to pick a stone up from a little pile by his feet. With exaggerated movement, he threw the stone high into the air, then turned away to pick up another as the first splashed down into the canal. He wore a grubby white jumper and brown flared trousers terminating a good two inches above black slip-ons, and was being watched by a small group on the opposite bank. Impassive, he crouched back on his heels, sprang upright and, windmilling his throwing arm, launched the next stone.

All this in silence, punctuated by the little splashes, and all under the gaze of the small band of observers, who smiled nervously. The thrower continued, with no great artistry or grace, his stones describing a random selection of arcs on their way into the oily water. Hong and I ran behind him, crossed the footbridge, and weaved our way through the spectators on the other side. We continued along the Hertford Union, under the A12, and on past Victoria Park. Joining the Regent's Canal at Old Ford, we turned south to head back alongside Mile End Park to Limehouse.

Away to our left, beyond the park, the tents of the five-ring circus were being quietly folded away, in the white stillness of an autumn afternoon in Stratford.

HENRY WILSON

GREENWICH CITY FARM

MATT HAYNES

THIS AFTERNOON, as I was standing on the corner of Greenwich Market gazing wistfully at the locked door of Ristorante Soteri and wondering, not for the first time, just how special the *chef's special* cottage pie had been, I noticed a sheet of A4 taped to the window bearing the logo of Mudchute City Farm. Now, there's lately been much debate around here about the chainification of Greenwich town centre – Nando's and Frankie & Benny's opening up at the Pierhead, and Jamie Oliver, bish-bosh, moving into the old Bar du Musée – but I never had Mudchute City Farm down as particularly expansionist; they always seemed perfectly happy over there on the Isle of Dogs, with their llamas and their sheep and their café serving up Tuscan sausages or vegetable crumble in a slightly ramshackle shed by the goat pens. So the idea that, even as I stood there peering at Signore Soteri's brutally stripped interior, teams of Gloucester Old Spots might be tugging trolleys laden with seasonal ingredients and locally sourced vegetables through the foot tunnel to a new culinary outpost in SE10, right next door to Goddard's Pie Shop, seemed an unlikely one.

That's assuming it was just the café that was branching out. But probably it would be, otherwise they'd have to apply for change of use from A3 to… whatever it is you need if you want to have live pigs. Which was a shame, as having live pigs in Greenwich was a grand idea. If they couldn't keep them in the shop, maybe they could put them across the road, in the grounds of the Old Royal Naval College?

As I was pondering this, three girls emerged out of the sun.

"Can we ask you some questions?" one said. "It's for school."

"OK," I said, shielding my eyes. Maybe I should ask *them* how they felt about the idea of live pigs in Greenwich?

"What did you think of the Olympics?" said the same girl, reading from a small printed strip of paper.

"I liked them," I said.

She turned and glared at the girl next to her.

"He says he liked them," said this second girl to the third, who nodded, and wrote something down on a piece of paper attached to a clipboard.

The first girl turned back to me.

"Are you proud that England held the games?"

"Pleased, not proud," I said. And I was going to go on to tell her why it's not really possible to be proud of something you've not yourself actually done, in the same way that I'm *pleased* to be British, and sometimes *relieved*, and often *grateful*, but never *proud*, because proud makes no sense. But she'd already turned to stare silently at the second girl, who was relaying my reply to the girl with the clipboard.

"He's pleased not proud."

I shrugged inwardly, and waited for the next question.

"Do you know how much it cost?"

"How much... no, not exactly, I..."

"He doesn't know," said the second girl to the third.

The first girl smiled brightly.

"Thank you very much," she said.

And off they trotted, leaving me staring once more at the piece of paper in the window (it was, I now realised, merely advertising various upcoming farm events). I decided I rather liked the idea of live pigs in the Naval College. On that bit of grass by the Old Brewery, perhaps?

I wonder if they'd been hired by Rio?

De Janeiro, not... Ferdinand.

No Football Without The O's

Matt Haynes

I GREW UP AROUND HERE...

In 1978, when the O's reached the FA Cup semi-finals, shops on Leyton High Road from Drapers Field to the Bakers Arms were decked out with flags and red bunting. There was even a special commemorative issue of the *Waltham Forest Guardian*. These days, now the old floodlights have gone, you could walk down the High Road and easily never guess that, just behind those nondescript rows of rooftops on the other side of Coronation Gardens, there is a football ground.

Standing on the terrace at Peterborough a couple of seasons ago, idly flicking through the programme to distract myself from striker Adam Boyd's clearly under-rehearsed ploy of trying to disconcert the Posh defence with a series of Bowie-esque mimes – man-pacing-fretfully-outside-tube-station-wondering-where-his-date-has-got-to seemed to be a favourite – I noticed that the match was sponsored by Peterborough City Council. Other places, I mused, take pride in their clubs – especially one-team towns like Newcastle, where almost everyone in Eldon Square on Saturday morning is a walking barcode, or Hull, where the Tigers' elevation to the Premiership a few seasons ago revitalised the city in a way not seen since the invention of the herring. But Leyton – or Waltham Forest – seems indifferent. And now, apparently, the Olympic Stadium – just an overhit cross from Brisbane Road – is to be given to West Ham. Boris Johnson says they're *the obvious candidates*. It's big, but they'll have no trouble filling it; not if, as mooted, they sell tickets to local kids at giveaway prices...

At school, we only ever went to watch Orient; it was cheaper than Arsenal or Spurs, and all you had to do was walk down the road – you didn't need to get the tube, you didn't need to get your dad to take you. But, even then, no one ever said they supported Orient; in the playground, the talk was all of Chelsea, Liverpool – and Dirty, Dirty Leeds. (Less so Manchester United, who weren't much cop back then, and even spent one season with the O's in division two; when they came to Brisbane Road, shops and pubs covered their windows not with flags and red bunting but roughly cut chipboard panels, because – in those dark days of cattle-truck football specials – United's travelling fans were feared far more than the team.)

People even supported West Ham, despite West Ham plainly being an Essex club, whose true rivals are Southend United and Colchester – nicking the O's *East, East, East London* chant fools no one. Orient's first ground was in Clapton, on the London bank of the Lea;

by the time you get out to West Ham, you can practically smell the shellfish and white shoe polish.

The big clubs can look after themselves, and the little clubs… can look at Sky Sports. That seems to be the attitude, and that's why the little clubs keep disappearing. Once upon a time there was a Leytonstone FC too, and you could, as a kid with no money, look down onto their Granleigh Road pitch from the westbound platform at Leytonstone High Road station. But then, having merged with Ilford to begat Leytonstone & Ilford, they sold the ground for housing and merged with Walthamstow Avenue to begat Redbridge Forest… who merged with Dagenham to begat Dagenham & Redbridge… who now play in League Two; which is nice for the undemanding folk of Corned Beef City, but leaves Leytonstone's football-loving souls bereft of fifth-class action. But who cares – they can just support West Ham, Spurs or Arsenal, can't they? Or the O's? Don't be silly. If you see a kid in a red shirt on the streets of E11, it will have *Rooney* on the back, not *Mooney* (gangly Irishman David Mooney has these days taken over Adam Boyd's hapless role of loitering without much intent). Given the choice, even David Mooney would probably choose not to have *Mooney* on the back of his shirt.

None of us really want the O's to move down the road to Stratford. 4,000 people (and a wyvern called Theo) in a stadium that holds 54,000 doesn't sound much fun. It would just be nice not to be ignored. But West Ham being given the stadium, simply because Boris Johnson has heard of them and doesn't know where Leyton is, and then filling it via seedy cheap-seat enticements – reaching out, as they say, to a whole new generation – could signal the end for London's second-oldest league club. Which would be an odd sort of Olympic legacy.

No Football Without The O's, says the banner draped across the back of the Tommy Johnston stand every other Saturday.

I hope that's right. I grew up around here…

Addendum 1
Since this piece was written, it has become apparent that,
although David Mooney used to be shite, he is in fact all right,
and we are walking in a Mooney wonderland.

Addendum 2
Since the above addendum was written, it has become apparent that I may
have been right the first time, and that there is only one Kevin Lisbie.

197

He's five, maybe six years old, and his small nose is pressed to the front window as they putter along the track towards Stratford. Until now, he's been mostly interested in other trains, first on the southbound DLR track but then, once they'd climbed the curve north of Bow Church, on the parallel lines into Liverpool Street: express trains from Norwich, stopping trains from Shenfield, long slow lines of dirty steel containers from Felixstowe – all have featured in the excited commentary he's provided for his father, seated two seats back. As they pass Pudding Mill Lane, though, he falls silent, his eye caught by the Olympic Park. The wings of the Aquatic Centre are being stripped and dismantled, bleak expanses of puddled tarmac are dotted with scaffolding poles and rusty yellow skips, and bulldozers are crawling over a muddy wasteland where, just months before, athletes had flexed and caught their breath and crowds queued for souvenirs. The boy considers all this. Then, at last, he glances back over his shoulder.

"Daddy," he says, "it looks like Stevenage."

IT'S JUST BEFORE NOON, and I'm standing in the cold on the bridge by the station. Two years ago, I moved here to Leyton with the boy I was with on the day of the bombs. We came here before the High Road was painted like a rainbow, before the streets were paved and cleaned for the few people that made it this far. Along with the locals who welcomed us, and the grit that never went away, my husband and I are still here.

Today, before I turn into the ticket hall, ice biting at the air, I see the Lea Valley, as always, stretching mistily into the West. Gone are the pink lips of temporary stands; soon, the Basketball Arena's pillowy swells of white PVC will go too. Left behind will be a curve of golden wood and a few fading silver signs that barely make an impact on the eye any more.

I think of summer, and a certain sound and tension moving through the air, of the things that have changed in seven years, and the things that haven't; of the things that went wrong, and the things that didn't. I think back to the day before that day in July 2005, to my former colleague and his grouchy complaints, and how his mind buckled, and his soul melted, after Danny Boyle's opening ceremony. I remember how easy it seemed to think beyond the sycophantic slogans, the politicking, the physical feats, and watch a different world emerging at the end of our high road. I remember how that peculiar Emerald City drew our gaze to it so wonderfully, and how it brought us together in genuine ways – graciously, warmly, collectively, inclusively. I hold my scarf about the knot, trying to hang onto that thought, as I move on.

It's just after nine. The next train to Lewisham is in three minutes. Good. No need to rush. I know it's in three minutes because it says so on the monitor at the end of the subway. Before the Olympics, we didn't have a monitor at the end of the subway; we just had the fear of the unknown and, on a good day, the thrill of the chase.

During the Games, Greenwich station swarmed with stewards, and Platform 2 was divided in half by a red and white ribbon to make sure those heading for the DLR didn't get entangled with those waiting for South Eastern services to Cannon Street. They even took away the Oyster card reader at the top of the stairs, in case it caused milling.

I was up at the Observatory just before Christmas. Below me, the lawn where the stadium had sat was still mostly mud, but the two paths crossing it diagonally were open again. Each was lined on both sides with bright plastic fencing. It looked like a giant St Andrew's flag. Clearly, returfing is going to take some time; the daft thing is, though, the new grass will probably look better than the old – it had grown pretty threadbare, to be honest.

On my way down, I found myself listening to the conversation of the couple on the path ahead of me. What a mess, they were saying, with all the mud and the plastic fences. Then the woman said: "Didn't they use it for the Olympics or something?"

Here comes my train, right on time. In less than three hours, it will be 2013. I'm glad we now have a train indicator – it's only a little thing, but it makes life less stressful.

I still wish they'd put the Oyster card reader back, though.

Alex
Farebrother
-Naylor

IMAGE CREDITS

The cartoons were all drawn by **Alex Farebrother-Naylor**.

The photos were mostly taken by **Matt Haynes**, but we'd also like to thank:

Eduard Popescu for letting us use the photos on pages 9 & 11;

Martin Deutsch for letting us raid his Flickr pages for the photos on pages 6, 16 (Marshgate Centre), 34, 39, 41, 42-3 (background), 96 (top), 103 (centre), 139 (top), 141 and 200-1;

and similarly **Gordon Joly** for the photos on pages 7, 12 (background), 16 (other than the Marshgate Centre), 28 and 33 (background).

Other photos were taken by **Lucy Munro** (pp64 & 135, top), **Chris Long** (pp104-5 & p139, bottom), **Jude Rogers** (p119), **Katherine Lloyd** (p123), **Luke Upton** (p126), **Matt Salusbury** (p131), **Phil Lenthall** (p140), **Rebecca Thomas** (p142), **Scott Cawley** (p144), **Robin Parker** (p151) and **Andrew Gray** (p155, noticeboard).

Ackroyd, Peter, failed circumambulation of 169
Adlington, Rebecca, confused with midget submarine 95
Americans: mistakenly in Warwickshire 14; easily impressed by Stoke Newington 32; on horses 55, 174; what can you say to them? 108; what you can say to them 110-1
Banshees 176-83
Basketball Arena: destruction of 200; destruction of Greenwich to enable survival of 80; destruction of ley lines during construction of 169
Beasts: mythical see banshees; fabulous see Wyvern, Theo; filthy see Johnson, Boris
Blackheath: fireworks 60-2; Tea Hut 60, 65; as possible venue for winter olympics 65; as possible venue for armageddon 79-81
Bolt, Usain: cavorting with 146; doing that thing he does 147; tweeting 152; breaking into Brisbane Road 152, 166
Bowie, David: trapped in imaginary phone box 195; trapped in imagined leggings 119
Burley, Aidan 107
Café Rouge: existentialism in 83-4; sadness at lack of one-legged Russians in 168
Cameron, David: unfounded allegations of sexual relations with horses 205; prime minister 2010-13
Cannon: Street station 6; loose see Johnson, Boris
Children: masochism of 147; defeatism of 150; unquenchable needs within hearts of 23; pointlessness of trying to have intelligent conversation with 57; inability to distinguish between Olympic Park and Stevenage 198

Chocolat: chaud 14; pain au 84
Coe, Seb: in Los Angeles 151; in Wenlock suit 146; in love with German expressionist cinema 69
Cotton, Fearne 84 see also pretty much everywhere
Cruise: Tom 142-3; missiles 79-81
Cycling: success of Team GB in 129, 133, 158; East Dulwich using a map of Clapham 174
Daley: Tom, 150; Thompson see Thompson, Daley
D.I.S.C.O. 127 see also Earth, Wind and Fire
Defence: Ministry of 79-81; Peterborough United's 195
Deptford Creek: use of in last days of Graf Spee 173; use of in last days of east London 74, 76
Dinosaurs: extinction of 90; see also Queen
DLR: absence of 14; presence of 198; closure of 90; separation of South Eastern Trains from 201; means of egress from 92
Dogs: Emily (dachshund) 173; Trevor (breed not specified) 176; poodle (plot device) 101; Isle of 99-101, 190, 192; hot 148; slum- 111; in hammocks 10; hunting with 50; angry 69; purchasing hats for 67; see also Doo, Scooby
Dong Dong see Dong, Dong
Dong, Dong 151
Doo, Scooby 150
Doo, Doobie Doobie see Sinatra, Frank
Düsseldorf 92, 135, 158
Dutch, overwhelming orangeness of 141, 149
Earth, Wind and Fire 81
Ephemerality: of human existence 80; of Basketball Arena 80, 200
Essex 102; true home of West Ham FC 195-6; paucity of ways to anywhere else 84

Existential: foreboding 84; disquiet 38
Farah, Mo 156-7; what he can do in 15 minutes 109; what he can do in 5 minutes see "Boiling an Egg with Mo Farah", BBC1, 8 p.m.
Fencing: blue 30, 40-1; plastic 91, 201; metal 45, 46; horses jumping over 55; being stared at by horses through 92; garden see www.wickes.co.uk
Fish: Island 97, 190; introduced to Turtle 51; shell- 196; gold- 166
Fuckwits 115-6 see also Burley, Aidan
Galloway: George 73; as source of hammocks 10
Greenwich: pigs in 192-3; residents' curious love of toboggans 65; life in during riots compared to Detroit 55; life in during Olympics compared to Nazi Germany 66
Greenwich station: way from 69; way to 91; way through 201
GRRRR 63, 125 see also dogs, angry
Guns: reality of 81; use of on pensioners 100; big fuck-off 138; children and 151; teenagers and 35; toddlers and 121
Hadid, Zaha 57
Haiku 121
Hackney Marsh see Marsh, Hackney
Hackney Wick see Wick, Hackney
Hackney Empire see press for details
Hands: giant foam 92, 118, 120-1, 128; Tom Cruise's 142-3; Tom Cruise's giant foam see a psychiatrist
Helicopters: on HMS Ocean 74, 76; leaving Saigon 90; intimidating pensioners with 100-1; ejection of HM Queen from 77, 106

Hippophile, unexpected use of in popular song 89

Hitler: scale model of 22; tasteless use of when losing all sense of perspective 66

Holmes: Kelly 6; Sherlock, absence of faeces when addressing 136

Horror 103 *see also* Northampton

Horses 44, 49, 123, 135; dancing 83; being stared at by 92; nudity and 55; giant purple 62, 69-70; talking 124; being jumped on by 51; last 175 *see also* Revelations, Book of; sexual fascination with 55 *see also* Cameron, David

Igglepiggle 61 *see also* Cameron, David

Index 204-5 *see also* Littlewoods

Johnson, Boris: rise to power 179-81; death of 176; carried off by angry seabirds 183; fucking 136; never heard of Leyton 196

Kebabish 133, 152, 153

Leyton Orient 13, 152, 166, 194-6; Division Three champions 1969-70

M&Ms *see* Smarties

Macarena 81

Macaroni 174

Mandela, Nelson 11

Mandeville 112, 146

Mandy Lifeboats *see* me after

Mars: Attacks 10; bars traded for SS officers 24

Marsh: Hackney 13-14, 28, 30, 74; Stratford 7; Kent 181-2; Rodney *see* QPR

McDonald's 161; biggest in world 140; use of as toilet 143; possible other uses of *entry not found*

MI6 [**entry deleted**]

Missiles: installation on tower blocks 73, 85, 101; installation on Blackheath Common 79; installation at home *see* instructions on box and if in doubt consult a qualified warmonger

Nanny: state 107; children's *see* Poppins, Mary

NHS, brilliance of 110

Northampton 49

Nudity: full 55; partial 170; **do not** *see also* Burley, Aidan

Olympic Games 1-208

Olympic Village: inaccessibility of 170; looks a bit like Magnitogorsk 98

Opening Ceremony 101, 102; participating in 115-7, 104-6; American take on 108; American take on witheringly dismissed 110-1; complete misjudgment of public response to *see* Burley, Aidan

Paralympic Opening Ceremony 163

Paralympic Closing Ceremony 166

Paralympics 163-6

Pigs: live 192-3; dead *see* Blackheath Tea Hut

Pointlessness: of cable car 81; of life 84; of Adam Boyd 195; *see also* Time Out

Poly, Thames 84

Poly, Toynbee *see* Guardian Corrections and Clarifications

Poppins, Mary: being cool 108; floating 116; naked *see* a therapist, seriously

Queen: of UK 77, 106, 111; of banshees 177; awful rock band, don't give me any of that irony nonsense 158

Rascal, Dizzee 111

Right-wing ideologues *see* Hitler, Adolf; War, Spanish Civil; Burley, Aidan

Rihanna: lack of umbrella 166; lack of Welshness 166

Self, Will 169, 172

Self, Immolation of (sudden urgent desire to perform) *see* Cotton, Fearne

Shooting: in Woolwich 35, 67, 151; in Dover 74;

of Father Christmas 22; of Cotton, Fearne *see* me in the alley at six, come alone

Sirens: ambulance 185; *see also* Rascal, Dizzee

Smarties (not M&Ms) 143

Sneezing, words that sound a bit like *see* Düsseldorf; Haiku; Zaha Hadid

Spice Girls 11

Testicles, unexpected appearance of 169

Thames Poly *see* Poly, Thames

Thompson, Daley 151

Time Out 38

Torch: Olympic 113-7, 150; song by Soft Cell 117; credit for use of lyrics of song by Soft Cell 116

Turtle, introduced to Fish *see* Fish, introduced to Turtle

Twitter 146; difficulty of using when having paws, 147; difficulty of using when being Usain Bolt 152; really good reasons for uninventing 67, 107

Victoria: station 114; Park 30, 155, 181; Pendleton 133; Beckham *see* Spice Girls; Wood (not that one) 68

War: Second World 22, 91; Iraq 179; Spanish Civil 73-4; Vietnam 101; what is it good for? 0

Wenlock: in Leicester Square 143; not in Olympic Park 145-7

Wick, Hackney 14, 176-83

Wind and Fire Earth *see* Earth, Wind and Fire

Winter: Olympics, organising of 65; Palace, storming of 90

Wonderland: entering a secret 27; walking in a Mooney 196

Woolwich: big screen in 154; very angry dog in 69; all-day breakfast in 154

Woolwich Dockyard 6

Woolwich Arsenal 6 Chelsea 0 (Walcott 23, 45, 67, 58, Terry o.g. 43, Wilshere 87)

Wyvern, Theo the 152, 194

SMOKE: A LONDON PECULIAR

… a love letter to London, to the wet neon flicker of late-night pavements, electric with endless possibility, and the soft dishevelled beauty of the city's dawn… to the overheard stories and unexplored histories, the facts and the fictions, the accidental poetry and fugitive art of graffiti-slashed suburban stations and rain-splashed shopfronts… the out-of-shot lives half glimpsed from a train window, or from a phone number scrawled on the back of a travelcard, dropped on the night-bus stairs…

In April 2003, Jude Rogers and Matt Haynes made a thousand copies of a small magazine with a black and white photo of Centre Point on the cover and a stripe as red as a 38 bus down one side. They took it round the capital's bookshops, explaining to bemused staff that it contained words and images inspired by the city in which they lived. Three issues later, the print run was five thousand, over eighty shops within walking distance of a station or bus stop were listed as stockists, and – somewhat reluctantly – the decision was taken to employ a proper distributor with a van.

After publishing sixteen issues, Matt and Jude reinvented *Smoke* as a website and began work on a variety of one-off projects. The first of these, *Soho!*, was a board game inspired by the two things for which that small, historic patch of London is famous around the globe: its pubs, and its one-way system. And the second you now hold in your hands.

New words and images are published regularly at

www.smokealondonpeculiar.co.uk

and that's also where you can find more information about Smoke projects old, new and hypothetical, plus details of how to contribute.

MATT HAYNES used to work in an NCP multi-storey in Bristol and, outside rush hour, wrote the music fanzine *Are You Scared To Get Happy?* – a heartfelt concoction of Pritt Stick and Letraset which successfully campaigned for the abolition of the compact disc. Three years studying theoretical physics taught him that reality was an endlessly malleable concept, something he then put to good use as co-owner of Sarah Records, an independent label which, it would be fair to say, changed the face of modern popular music; sadly, the world isn't fair. Born in Leytonstone of good Bethnal Green stock, he is a lifelong Leyton Orient supporter, so has never taken much interest in top-quality sporting activity performed by elite athletes in peak physical condition; indeed, as a lifelong Leyton Orient supporter, such things tend to upset him. After some years being unsure whether he lived in Kennington or Vauxhall, he decided to move to Greenwich with his cat, Schrödinger. Sadly, on arrival in SE10, Schrödinger turned out not to be in her pet carrier after all, and is still either missing or dead or both. Matt likes to think of himself as a man of mystery, but won't tell anyone why.

JUDE ROGERS used to work for an unpleasant charitable organisation up a fire escape in Acton, from where, in an attempt to bring back her will to live, she emailed a man she'd met at a gig, suggesting they start a fanzine about London. A year later, she was employed by some people at *The Word* magazine, who'd seen a copy and found her amusing. Since then, she's written for the *Guardian, Observer, Times, Q, New Statesman, Elle, Red, The Quietus* and *Caught By The River*, and broadcast regularly and Welshly on the BBC. Claims to fame: Paul McCartney has rung her mobile, Martin Amis has laughed at her jokes (or was it wind?), and Robert Plant, Björk and Tony Benn have made her tea (Tony used Value bags – he said that proper tea was theft). Jude once told her husband that her highlight of 2011 was interviewing Michael Stipe; he pointed out that they also got married that year. She also judged the Mercury Music Prize for six years, but The Klaxons' win was not her fault. Born and bred in Swansea, she's lived in almost every part of north and east London since 1999, but has now settled in Leyton; the school at the end of her road, mysteriously, is where Matt went. Or was it?